AWAKEN YOUR INNER PHYSICIAN

Awaken Your

INNER PHYSICIAN

the "Missing Links" in Health Care

Holistic Practices for Physical Pain,
Mental Health and Emotional Well-Being

GERILYN VAN

MA, CMT, RMT, CYT

LUMINARE PRESS

WWW.LUMINAREPRESS.COM

Printed in the United States of America

Luminare Press
442 Charnelton St.
Eugene, OR 97401
www.luminarepress.com

LCCN: 2022901343
ISBN: 978-1-64388-848-4

DEDICATIONS

"Awaken Your INNER PHYSICIAN... the 'Missing Links' in Health Care"
*is dedicated to the well-being of our future generations of children,
in hopes that the information in this book may someday be taught as a
primary part of the Health Education Curriculum in our school system.
It is my understanding that an Integrated Health Care Curriculum would
address the opioid and mental health crisis, and the lack of emotional
intelligence, that has created so many unhealthy, violent and
addiction-related behaviors in our youth and society today.*

*I also dedicate this book to my dear friend, Perry Bream, who died while
"Awaken Your INNER PHYSICIAN" was in the final editing and beginning
publishing stages. Perry's death happened due to the mental illness and
emotional disturbances of a dearly beloved individual. I believe if our
school system had had a comprehensive, Integrated Health Curriculum,
starting in kindergarten, one that provided practices for mental and
emotional health, alongside our traditional health education which
includes nutrition and exercise, Perry's life could have been spared.*

*Perry read "Awaken Your INNER PHYSICIAN" and wrote the beautiful
recommendation below. After reading the book, Perry told me that
many of the practices and the affirmation, "I deeply and completely love
and accept all my life's lessons and soul's journey without exception"
were very healing for him. Sending you love Perry, and thank you for
being an integral part of the purpose of this book in so many ways.*
—GERILYN VAN

"*The nature of all pain is unique and personal. Yet, what Gerilyn relates to
us in 'Awaken Your INNER PHYSICIAN' is likely to resonate with whatever may disturb our own lives. She opens doors into spaces where body,
mind and soul all play a role in the Inner Physician. The book elevates our
own resources to a profound, elemental level of healing from within.*"
—PERRY BREAM, merchant mariner and software developer

CONTENTS

HOW TO USE THIS BOOK
TO MAXIMIZE YOUR BENEFITS

1. *Awaken Your INNER PHYSICIAN ... the "Missing Links" in Health Care* is not meant to be read quickly. Give yourself ample time to pause, reflect and absorb the deeper truths in the chapters before trying the practices at the end of each chapter. Each chapter has two elements, the author's personal story, followed by various wellness practices. (Except for Chapter 1, which is just my story.)

2. After reading a chapter, try one wellness practice a day/ night. There are 3 practices per chapter, so you might want to stretch them out over the week. If you feel inspired to do two practices, then please do so. Just don't rush through them. Go at a pace that will allow you to fully experience the practices. You may want to do some of the practices with a friend or partner, so you can read them to each other.

3. When you're done with the practices, circle the ones that you really enjoy so you can go back to them later and incorporate them into your daily wellness routines.

4. After you are finished with the book and practices, check out the Health and Well-Being Support Group Section near the end of the book. See if there are any groups, classes or teachers you may be interested in. Many of them are free and online.

Please note, the different healing modalities and practices do not need to be used in any particular order. If you are drawn to a specific healing modality, feel free to skip around to different chapters. Also, after you are done reading the book, the modalities can be used in combination with each other and modified according to your needs. Have fun with this. An example of combining practices would be while meditating, use breath awareness, present touch with your hands, music in the background and perhaps some simple inner inquiry questions.

This book is intended to be a life-enhancing resource and supportive guide to understanding mental, emotional and physical health for yourself, your family and all the people you love.

INTRODUCTION

I WAS PUT TO THE TEST OF A LIFETIME WHEN I WENT THROUGH TWO and a half years of severe chronic pain. During this time, I met with various dentists, doctors, oral surgeons and other specialists - seventeen in all. They all had differing opinions and recommendations. My anxiety and stress levels were high due to the pain and the unknown. I often became frustrated with the doctors because many of them didn't listen to me. I had to make important decisions around what to do regarding my pain, body, teeth and finances. This meant constantly calming my nervous system, soothing the pain and clearing my mind.

As a holistic healing practitioner and school teacher, it was my turn to use all the tools I had learned, practiced and taught the last thirty years. I listened to my inner guidance daily and used all the "INNER PHYSICIAN" practices that I had picked up through various classes, workshops, teachers and books. These tools greatly reduced my doctor visits and dependency on medications. Ultimately, that meant less of my time and money was wasted. Unlike medication, these holistic practices have zero negative side-effects and cost nothing to use. The practices in this book also helped me stay out of depression and keep my spirits lifted through one of the most challenging times in my life.

Of course, there were times in the process that I needed medication and surgery, and I am grateful for the expertise of the doctors. However, doctors don't know everything nor do they have time to deal with the daily stresses, physical pain, and emotional healing

I needed during and after surgeries. Medication, painkillers and other costly mechanism were most often the first solution the doctors offered and sometimes even insisted for my pain. There were times when I said "no" to the doctors and continued to use my holistic approaches in dealing with the pain. I educated many doctors and nurses on holistic ways to deal with pain, mentally, emotionally and physically. Meditation, energy awareness, emotional care (identifying emotions and asking for my needs to be met), present touch, positive affirmations, nature connection, soothing music and inner inquiry questions, were some of the practices that I used. I was amazed at the lack of education around these alternative methods.

Interestingly, the pain was the impetus for one of the greatest spiritual awakenings I've ever experienced. This awakening came from surrendering to my soul's journey, learning to embrace pain, and to love and accept what is, from a place of awareness. In this way, I connected to something greater than the physical, mental and emotional pain. I connected to what I call my Higher Self, my true Self. This Higher Self is untouched by any pain or any situation. This place of awareness, Self, has always been and will always be a part of my soul's ever-unfolding journey and gives me the greatest peace and joy in life.

Chapter 1

A SOUL'S UNIQUE JOURNEY WITH PAIN

"We cannot always direct the wind.
But we can adjust the inner sails."

THOMAS S. MONSON

WHY ME? I ASKED MYSELF AS TEARS STREAMED DOWN MY FACE. The pain in my mouth, head and teeth was overwhelming. I had another dentist appointment in a week, but had to bear the pain until then. Fear started to creep in as I lay in my bed, eyes closed, in my small cottage in the redwoods. *What is going on?* After several visits, my dentist, Dr. Par, tried to re-adjust my bite, hoping it would resolve the problem. It didn't. Only lying down and surrendering to my cushy bed and soft pillows felt comforting. I laid still and observed the discomfort in my mouth. There wasn't just one specific ache in one tooth, but in many teeth, mainly in my back molars. The pain would come and go, but was getting more intense in a couple of the teeth. I would observe which molar had the most pain while lying in my bed sometimes for hours. If my dentist couldn't figure it out, I would!

Will I be able to work? I enjoyed my part-time nanny position working four hours a day for a wealthy couple with a ten-year-old boy and a dog. The thoughts kept pouring through. *How will I be able to eat?* The pain was affecting my bite. It hurt to bite down and there were only a few points of contact where I could chew. *I love to eat. Maybe I'll lose my job!* I was needing more breaks throughout the day because of the pain. *How will I support myself?* I had no one to financially lean on. I was single and on my own. *A loving, wealthy, supportive partner would have been nice, but I have to work. I'm going to need to do this one on my own.* A little pity and sadness came over me.

I felt alone. Tears and then more tears streamed down. Then I reminded myself, *I may not be rich, but I have a wealth of tools.* After all, I was a holistic teacher who had taught others various healing modalities. I had even owned my own health and well-being business several years ago, offering Reiki, Massage, Life Coaching and other healing practices. Now it was my turn. I knew I would need these tools more than ever. My mood became a bit more positive. I curiously pondered, *there is something I can learn from all of this. But what?*

The pain would come and go, and often it was intense. And then there was the *unknown*, the unpredictable, setting my nerves on fire. I could manage the pain, but not the *unknown*.

I would be with the pain and nurture it by relaxing my body and gently placing my hands on the pain while tapping into a loving stream of energy until the pain subsided. The pain woke me in the middle of the night. In the morning, I would rest deeply, relaxing my body before going to my job as a Nanny. While at work, I took as many breaks as I could, nurturing the pain in my jaw and teeth. My car became my haven as I took constant breaks before and after all of the boys' activities, laying back in the driver's seat, sitting with the pain and tuning inward until I felt a river of loving energy.

My dentist, Dr. Par, was at the end of his rope as the scope of my pain was beyond his understanding. On one of my visits to see him regarding the pain, I sat in his office and explained to him that the pain was becoming more intense in one of my molars and my jaw was beginning to hurt as well. "Gerilyn, you have chronic pain and TMJ. I suspect you may need orthognathic (jaw) surgery." My whole body cringed. *What? I've never had problems with my jaw before. No, no, not jaw surgery.* The resistance on my face was obvious. He looked at me quite sternly and said, "I know you don't want to face this, but seriously, you need to look into orthognathic surgery and here is a pamphlet on TMJ. Your bite keeps shifting and the pain isn't going to stop." He gave me a few more pamphlets and suggested I do some research on my own.

First he tells me I have TMJ, a label that I wasn't about to take on. *How can this be? I had a bite that worked fine for 50 years and had never had problems with my jaw or bite before this!* Resistance to his words ran deep. *What does he know?* And then I softened. *He is the doctor and I am experiencing pain every day. I guess he knows more than I do. But please don't label my pain as chronic.* It brought my spirits down to think I might have this pain forever. After some reflection, I surrendered a bit more to the doctor and his knowledge. *I'll do anything to get rid of the pain and have a stable bite, even if it means jaw surgery.* I decided to do some research about orthognathic surgery and face my fears. I called a girlfriend and told her of my situation.

"Find the gift in it," my friend said.
Those words would play back again and again.

How to embrace pain as a gift? I never wanted pain, physically, emotionally or mentally for that matter. I didn't go seeking it out. In fact, to some degree or another I tried to stay away from pain. Surgery meant more pain and I wasn't leaning into it too quickly. I didn't have much control or much knowledge about what was going on in my mouth. That was the hard part. But at least, there was a possible end to my pain. I felt some hope as I began researching orthognathic surgery.

I called the offices of surgeons who specialized in jaw surgery. After talking to a few, I became somewhat comfortable with the idea of surgery. It was a procedure that would only take a day, and then I'd be an inpatient for a couple of days. I began accepting it slowly. *But the cost!* I was shocked. I remained quiet on the phone as I listened to the quotes. *What!?! $32,000 for just the upper jaw. $64,000 for both upper and lower. There was no way I could afford either!* And I didn't have insurance that covered this sort of thing. I had several thousand in my savings and a small piece of land. I cried. This was my retirement and life savings.

I began trying to figure it out. *I would have to sell my land which would be about the same price as the surgery.* Just thinking about it gave me a stomach ache. I began feeling sorry for myself. *I am just a nanny, an honorable one at that.* Tears came down. *I just don't make that kind of money.* I continued evaluating my financial situation and how I would pay for it. Then I would reassure myself. *I could always borrow money if I had too. Maybe my parents could help me out. I'll make it somehow.* The pain began to arise again so I laid down and began massaging my jaw.

I felt sad and alone, and knew this was *my* journey, and no one could do it for me.

Dr. Par was an okay dentist with a friendly persona. But he also a down side. He didn't listen very well and would skip over my questions. It was frustrating. However, he explained he had a hard time answering questions because of the chaotic nature of the office. He suggested I call him and send letters with the questions I had so he could take time to answer my questions. I thought about the possibility that my bite was just off. I didn't want surgery if I could help it. So I wrote him a letter asking for a recommendation for a specialist who could help me with my bite.

He called me back. "Hello Gerilyn. After reading your letter, I suggest your next step be with Dr. Join and Dr. Nelson. Your case is a difficult one. Dr. Join is an orthodontist and can assist in helping realign your bite and his office is right down the street. Dr. Nelson, on the other hand, is a highly specialized prosthodontist who used to share our office space. He seemed like a real nice guy. I think you'll like him and he also has an office nearby. He specializes in proper occlusion and difficult cases. They are better suited to address the pain issues in your teeth and give you a new bite than I am." I called that day to schedule an appointment with both of them. My spirits were high. I had hope again.

I called Dr. Join's office and was able to get an appointment that week. When I arrived, his secretaries were very friendly. It felt like home. My gut however, wasn't sure I really needed his services. After all, my bite was fine before the pain started. There I was though, taking x-rays with his assistants. Then Dr. Join walked in carrying some paperwork. "Hello, Gerilyn. Let's see how we might help you. It looks as if your teeth might have been ground down. Maybe a night-guard may help. There are other treatment plans with the possibility of braces I can offer as well, but let's start here." he said confidently.

"Dr. Join, I don't really think I need braces. I've had this bite for over 50 years and it's worked fine. I just have pain in a few teeth and ...." Dr. Join seemed to understand my rationale.

"Well, let's try a night-guard." Dr. Join left and his assistant came in and made a mold for the bottom part of my teeth. He came back afterwards and instructed "You can pick it up next week."

Two weeks later, I felt optimistic as I drove for the first time to Dr. Nelson's office. His office was located in a ritzy, high class building. As I walked in the building, I noticed the expensive, modern furniture and the upscale interior. It was all a bit too much for my taste. Regardless, he offered the specific kind of treatment that I needed. As I approached the front desk, I could hear the ladies behind it talking. They stopped their conversation for a moment to welcome me and asked me to fill out new patient paperwork. As I filled out the forms, I could hear one of them complaining about her life and her boyfriend.

Yikes, drama! Negative energy.
**I didn't want to be rude,
but I had to get away from it.
The pain I was experiencing had
made me very sensitive.**

I handed my papers in and told the people at the front desk that I was going outside and to come and get me when the doctor was ready. I stood outside enjoying the sun and trees as my body relaxed. *Ahhhhh. Perhaps they have no idea how sensitive I am.* I stood there for several minutes. The same woman who was complaining came out and said "Gerilyn, please come with me inside for some x-rays." She gave me little eye contact and herded me into the x-ray room. "There, now you can go have a seat over here. The doctor will be in shortly." She motioned toward the adjacent room, curtly ushered me in and left the room.

I sat in the seat feeling disconnected to her and was hoping the doctor would be more present with me. I sat there preparing my mind for our conversation. More of the unknown. When Dr. Nelson came in, he was happy and cheerful. "Hello Gerilyn. So you were referred to me by Dr. Par." I proceeded to tell him about my situation and the pain in my back molars and jaw. He took some time to observe my bite and the x-rays.

Within minutes he offered me a treatment plan of putting crowns on 16 of my teeth to create a new bite. "So you don't think I need jaw surgery?" I was excited. "No, I don't." My spirits were up. "How much would it cost?" I asked. He proceeded to give me a quote of $28,000 for sixteen new crowns which included creating a proper occlusion. "I think that will take care of the pain," Dr. Nelson explained. "Wow, that's a lot of money." I was feeling concerned about forking out so much money. "But the pain would be gone, huh?" I asked. "I can't guarantee that, but you will have a bite and we can do this all in two visits." "Really?" I was feeling hopeful. "Two visits?" He nodded. I allowed him to create a mold of my teeth.

"So what do you think the problem is? Dr. Par thinks I need orthognathic surgery." I filled him in on what Dr. Par had told me.

"I don't think that is the problem. I think we can fix the problem with your bite. And most likely it will take care of the pain." As I attempted to ask more questions, he hurried me along. He began putting his things away and darted toward the open door space while speaking, "So let me know of your decision."

"Uh, what about some financial assistance... and I was wondering about…" I tried again to ask some questions and connect a little more with him, to see if he was the right doctor for me.

"Talk to the front desk." And Dr. Nelson was gone. I sat there for a moment unsatisfied with his quick exit and then went to the front desk, paid them and told them the doctor said their might be some financial assistance. What they offered was more of a loan than any financial discount.

"Okay," I said. "I'll call you and set up my next appointment."

While driving home, doubt and confusion set in. *He said, "No guarantee." If I start this process with him, what if it doesn't work? The pain was in my teeth. How would a new bite take care of that? Then I would have invested a lot of money.* Something didn't quite add up. *He wouldn't stay around and answer questions and I could hardly stand sitting in the waiting room with the gossip.* I felt uncomfortable with the visit. *But at least he said he didn't think I needed orthognathic surgery.*

The doubts kept rising. I needed to go inward and think about all of it. *Maybe he's not the right doctor. But what do I know? I can hardly pronounce the word prosthodontist.* I felt a twinge in my heart and my gut was unsettled. My gut was speaking to me. I had to buckle up and go within as I weighed this out before investing so much time, money and energy. Dr. Par's advice about orthognathic surgery and Dr. Nelson's advice about recapping all my teeth and not needing orthognathic surgery contradicted each other.

Who to trust? **Beyond the doctor's advice was my deeper inner wisdom.**

When I truly listened, felt into my body and heart and questioned Dr. Nelson's proposal, the energy in my body contracted. There was a soft, subtle sensing, a kinesthetic testing of my body that was beyond the intellectual reasoning. When I said Dr. Nelson's name and proposal, my body would tighten, saying, *no, not him.* The reasoning was there too. Capping all my teeth was not going to fix the underlying pain I felt around and in my teeth. That left me with Dr. Par's recommendation of getting orthognathic surgery; but not yet. The thought of the surgery was unsettling in my body and didn't make complete sense either. *If my molars were aching and other teeth were not, how would jaw surgery help that? It wasn't my jaw that was bothering me, it was my teeth. And my bite had been fine for 50 plus years.* Something wasn't quite right and neither of their expert opinions made total sense. Some anger arose.

When I did express my ideas and concerns, Dr. Par didn't listen very well. And Dr. Nelson didn't seem to have time for my deeper questions and concerns. I expressed my frustration and sadness about my situation alone in my room as I dealt with the pain that was now rising every hour.

My neck was beginning to get tight too. *Of course, it's all connected - my teeth, jaw and neck.* Being a massage therapist, I knew that. Laying down, relaxing, nurturing the pain and then getting up was the only thing that helped me get through the day. My family and friends' concerns meant a lot to me, but there was not much anyone could do. I knew I would be facing this one alone. At a deeper level, it seemed like this was a test of my soul, an initiation of sorts. Me, my teeth, my pain, the doctors and the financial burden were mine to figure out. I put all my energy and attention into at least keeping my job. My social life would need to take a back seat. I had to take care of myself and manage the pain until this problem was resolved.

At times, the pain in my mouth and jaw and neck was so great that it was difficult for me to even talk. One day, the child I took care of daily, whom I called "my nanny-boy" was talking about his school day. He noticed I wasn't responding. "You're not talking much. How come?" he asked. "I'm just really tired these days and don't feel like talking much." I didn't want the main focus to be on my pain so I hid it as best I could. My nanny-boy didn't really know what I was going through. He seemingly understood the lack of words and probably appreciated it; less preaching and telling him what to do. I chose my words carefully and learned to say just what was needed in the moment. There was a gift in that.

The job was only four hours a day. I could manage it. Extra breaks on my job while no one was looking meant I would leave the room when my nanny-boy was doing homework and rest in the living room. I would take longer resting periods dealing with my pain in the car as I waited to pick him up from school. Also, he was getting older and needed less of my attention, so that helped. And the dog would just have to be walked less. And I could bite on the molars that didn't ache. At the end of a week, I was amazed! Somehow, I had managed to get through it, pain and all.

The next morning, I had my last appointment with my orthodontist, Dr. Join. He was a kind and gentle soul, but there was nothing more he could do for me professionally. *Why spend thousands on rearranging my teeth when I don't know what is causing the pain?* I shared with him how I could no longer eat crunchy foods. Eating was getting difficult. I could no longer eat my favorite foods like pizza, sushi and salad. When I told him, he had a great suggestion. "You're going to have to get used to eating soft foods for a while. A juicer helped my wife through a difficult time. She had a year when she couldn't eat. The juicer was the main way she was able to consume enough nutrients." I appreciated this tip.

My orthodontist had done all he could, which really wasn't anything, except for confirming the fact that I didn't need braces. I knew it and now so did he. Part of the process I guess. Part of me knew it was a waste of time and money to see him. The night-guard wasn't making any difference. But Dr. Par recommended him. I didn't completely trust my own intuition beyond the doctors' advice. I was also just learning the ropes of how the "system" worked… lots of recommendations to various specialists.

I went back to Dr. Par's office and he saw the pain I was in. His next recommendation was Dr. Black, an oral surgeon. I told him about Dr. Nelson's treatment plan. Dr. Par was concerned and not in agreement with Dr. Nelson's plan. "Check out Dr. Black. He is an oral surgeon."

I called Dr. Black's office right away. Dr. Black had an opening for an initial consultation the very next day. It was moving along smoothly, a good sign. At the consultation, Dr. Black did a few diagnostic tests and saw how great the pain was. He offered to extract the tooth right away and give me an implant. Implants are expensive. Having hope felt good and out-weighed the financial cost. I was so happy to think my tooth might be gone, along with the pain. He was able to fit me in the next day.

The assistant soon prepared me for the surgery. "I've been through something similar," she said." It's really difficult when there is pain around the teeth, because it is so close to your brain." She was very supportive. I laid back in the surgical chair and surrendered. Dr. Black came in and gave me a local anesthetic. I was more than ready to be rid of the intense pain. He extracted my molar with some tugging and pulling and put my first-ever implant in place. He told me to wait six months before getting a crown. I walked out of his office a happy, hopeful patient, with some Tylenol, a couple penicillin and a numbed, half of a smile. *Dr. Black was my angel,* I thought to myself.

Over the next few days, in that area where the tooth was pulled, the pulsating pain had lessened. Unfortunately, there was a different irritating pain with the implant. After a few weeks, I called Dr. Black and told him about the stabbing pain with the implant. He explained that it might be affecting a nerve and it may take longer for the pain to go away completely. *Be patient,* I told myself. I sat with the irritating sensations in my implant in hopes it would go away. I also had mild pain on the other side of my mouth with two of the back molars. That pain was not as intense, but was still there. I spent a lot of time being with the pain as I massaged my gums. I knew I would need to address it if it got any worse. For now however, I needed to resolve the most intense pain first.

One evening while resting in my cottage, laying in my bed and comforting my body, my landlord called. "Gerilyn, I have some news that is difficult to tell you. My daughter is coming back to town and needs a place to land. I'm going to offer her the cottage and so I need you to move out. There is no hurry as you have a few months before she moves in. I'm sorry to break this news to you." I took a deep breath and sucked it up. "No problem. I understand." I hung up the phone and laid back down. *How untimely!* More of the unknown. I laid still, resting my head on my soft pillows, comforting the anxiety rising in my body.

"Surrender. Surrender," I would hear.
***To what?* I pondered.**
"This moment and the energy that moves through you.
Surrender and take the next step."

Life became quite simple - be with the pain, nurture and then get up. At a visceral level, I was learning to surrender, listen to my inner voice and love myself above all else. It was a repetitive lesson as I sat with the pain every morning, every day, not knowing what my next step would be. I followed the expansive energy, beyond the pain. The drive to stay in love with life, with myself, with my pain, with the many doctors, dentists and specialists was my greatest challenge.

One thing was for sure, I knew I didn't want to burden anyone or create any "bad karma." I had a strong understanding that what comes around goes around. For whatever reason, this was part of my journey and I was going to embrace it as best as I could. I decided to share my dilemma with a few close friends, but only them.

I didn't like the pity and sad face I'd get from most people. "Ohhh, that's terrible," or "I hope you will be okay." Energetically, it drained me to have to explain things and reassure people that I would be okay. I was very careful with whom I shared my journey. I chose those who could sit with me and embrace what was happening to me without projecting their fears and offering advice. I chose friends who were neutral and who saw me beyond this situation.

I had some cathartic cries about my situation, and once in a while I indulged in a pity party. I was authentic with my close friends. The sadness came and went. The anxiety about not knowing where this path was leading me would come and go too.

Along with the unknown, I felt a warm blanket of love surrounding me that kept me going, even when I was in pain.

I now had gone to see several doctors, a dentist, an orthodontist, a prosthodontist and an oral surgeon to address the pain in my molars and bite. The physical pain in my mouth, jaw and neck was intense and constant. I guess that's why the doctors called it "chronic pain." The pain in my jaw and neck were present off and on. I woke up to pain, managed it throughout the day and woke up to it again in the middle of the night. I had had a tooth pulled and unfortunately, the new implant caused a stabbing pain that wouldn't go away.

At times, I was easily annoyed because of the pain. I did my best not to extend my negativity to anyone but often found it leaking out in my thoughts towards the doctors when I didn't feel seen or heard. I could see how depression could easily find its way in. I nurtured myself and tried to stay focused on my next step as I looked for the "gift" in this situation, staying open to the possibilities.

Within a month, I found a spacious rental unit near the ocean. I needed those calming waves nearby to nourish my soul and soothe the pain. The space had an area for a small garden and an open view of rolling green hills. A friend helped me move. Little by little, I unpacked. I was amazed I had enough energy. Late at night, I laid still in my new home and listened to the ocean stirring, feeling deeply relaxed and surrendered.

Chapter 2

FINDING THE GIFT IN PAIN

"My body is my teacher.
It is telling me what I am feeling and
lets me know what I am ignoring or denying."

ANNE HILLMAN

MY BODY CONTRACTED WITH FEAR WHEN I FIRST HEARD THE WORD "chronic pain" from my dentist. Thinking of having pain for the rest of my life was not something I wanted to embrace. I had dealt with physical pain various times in my life, but no one ever labeled it "chronic."

Nobody really wants to be in pain. No one purposely chooses it. (Unless you are a sadomasochist of course, but that's a different subject.) If you are a human being with a body, heart and mind, pain is an inevitable part of life. Whether it be physical, emotional or mental, all of us experience pain of some kind or another. Most of us try to avoid pain. We often numb and distract ourselves from pain instead of addressing the deeper issues behind it. We avoid our pain in any number of ways, staying busy, suppressing emotions and using substances of all kinds are some of the most common ways. To one degree or another, we all do this.

Pain comes with different levels of intensity and can last for an hour, weeks, months and even years. Pain can be caused by physical injury, like a scratch, bump, sprain, dislocated hip or can come from an illness such as cancer. Emotional pain can occur due to stress, family or relationship issues, financial insecurity, the

Awaken Your Inner Physician

ending of a relationship or death of a loved one. These situations can trigger frustration, resistance, sadness, anxiety, depression and a host of other "negative" emotions. We try to avoid negative emotions. There are some people who even think these emotions are "bad"... if it *feels* "bad," it must *be* "bad." That assumption is made because many of us don't know how to express our emotional pain in a healthy way or listen for the underlying messages pain can bring. Our thoughts can create pain as well. Thoughts can be obsessive, self-destructive or negative. We often become attached to our ideas or judgmental thoughts about our self or others, and project them onto the world creating disconnect and separation.

**Even hearing the words "pain" and "chronic pain"
triggered fear in me and made my body contract.**

As I observed the contractions, a friend pointed out that if I simply changed the language and used the words "sensations" or "intense sensations" instead of "chronic pain," then my resistance to pain wouldn't perhaps get the best of me. I began to see that pain was merely an experience of energy, of sensations in my body. The pain wasn't who I was and it wasn't permanent. When I closely observed the sensations of pain, they would come and go. Even if the sensations lasted for a long time, they weren't present every second of every day like my mind had told me. This discovery helped me be present with the pain in my body for longer periods of time. I slowly began to relate to the pain without judgment or fear. In fact, I learned to observe the tightness, contractions, heaviness, the buildup of pressure in my mouth, jaw and neck with loving kindness and this helped me stay engaged in my healing process.

**The questions now became,
"What are these sensations (pain) teaching me?
How do I accept pain with gratitude?
And what might I learn from it?"**

To find the gift in pain meant being curious about the physical sensations I was experiencing and to hold my pain with love. As I explored the sensations and was present in my body without wanting them to be different than they were, they often softened. It was as if I was putting a ring of tenderness around the pain (sensations). As my fears lessened, I was able to explore and stay connected to my body with fascination while staying open to the possibilities of healing. By saying "yes" and surrendering to the pain (sensations), I was able to listen to what it needed.

When we say "yes" to pain, fear often arises, the fear that the pain will never go away, that it will solidify and stay if we say "yes." Saying "yes" to pain simply means being a friend to it and being present while exploring the sensations, emotions or thoughts as they arise. When pain is held in the arms of gentle curiosity, it can be observed, nurtured, and loved. Then insight and lessons can be learned. The pain may eventually dissolve, go away or become manageable; but that is *not* the focus. Sometimes the lessons come quickly and other times they can take hours, days, years and sometimes, a lifetime of practice. No matter how long it takes, embracing pain with gentleness is a healthy, everyday practice.

However, in our society, we are taught to avoid pain and to cover it up. This is because exploring and giving presence to our bodies, our emotions and thoughts takes time and can be uncomfortable. We often resist it. Our school system, our health care system and sometimes even our parents do not model or show us how to be with pain. Most of us do not therefore, give ourselves permission to be with pain when it arises. In fact, we are taught both directly and indirectly at a young age to suppress our negative feelings. We are told to be "happy." Instead of learning to be with negative emotions in a healthy way, we offer our children superficial "rewards" such as candy, donuts, cookies, toys, gadgets or a trip to the park to suppress their emotions. We also punish them and take away "rewards" if they aren't displaying positive emotions.

As a result of this training, as adults most of us try to suppress our negative feelings such as sadness, grief, anger and disappointment. We also are taught to take pills when physical pain arises. Our doctors and the pharmaceutical companies promote painkillers through commercials on TV and show us a "happy" lifestyle. We use over the counter medications, doctor prescribed medications, marijuana, caffeine, sugar, alcohol, cigarettes, porn, sex, gossip, shopping, excessive working, along with a host of other substances and behaviors to keep us from feeling and being present with our painful emotions and physical bodies. The overuse of these substances often lead to addictions that harm us physically, emotionally and mentally, and have a negative affect on our relationships and create havoc in our society.

In order to experience pain as a gift, we need to learn to sit and be present with it. Learning to observe ourselves without judgment as we become aware of pain and what is behind the pain takes time and patience. Often times, we want a quick fix, but learning life-long tools will help us in the greater journey of life. Meditation, healing energy, massage, breathwork and presence in nature, mindful movement and stretching, healing music, and inner inquiry, allow for deeper root causes and emotions to reveal themselves and healing to take place. This takes deep listening and carving out sacred time with our Self.

Sometimes, we lose sense of our Self, when we believe that we *are* the pain. Instead of observing the sensations, the pain, we sometimes end up identifying with the pain so much so that we get lost in it. We aren't taught how to be with pain so we attach to it and believe it is who we are. By doing so, we inadvertently add more pain, emotionally, physically and mentally to the situation. By learning to observe pain, we see it as an experience we are having rather than mistaking the pain for who we are.

**There were many times I wanted
the pain to be gone. *Now!***

I even used my tools with assertive intention. I tried massaging it out. I used great intentions and tried to direct a lot of healing energy to the painful areas. My body would become even tenser than it already was as I tried to heal myself'. It didn't take long for me to see what I was doing was counterproductive and caused more physical tightness, anxiety, frustration and discomfort.

There was a time I thought the doctors had the answer or could heal me. I wanted the doctors' appointments to come quicker. There was a certain urgency and pressure that would build up inside as I found myself becoming dependent on them for my well-being. This belief created more tension in my body and again, more discomfort.

> **The doctor's knowledge might have been
> interesting, but knowledge didn't make the pain
> go away nor did the pills they prescribed
> offer a permanent, healthy solution.**

Only by giving my body sweet presence and going within, knowing I had my own answers, would the tightness relax and open for greater healing. I learned that only by surrendering and being in a relaxed state could more healing energy come my way. I teetered on the edges of fascination with this healing energy and with the pain in my body. As I lay in bed, I would observe the pain. When I could remember that I am not the pain, but it was merely part of the experience I was having (and certainly not my essence), I could come back to center. Eventually my body and the pain would relax, soften and clarity would come. After that, I would get up with some joy in my next step.

It can be uncomfortable and difficult to sit with oneself and the pain body. Through the softest, most intimate lens, we can learn to embrace even the most difficult circumstances of pain. The space around the thoughts, around the pain, and the fear eventually take a back seat. By surrendering and being still with our self, each moment becomes a new journey. The acceptance of pain becomes a part of our life's experience. Only by embracing pain can loving life force energy soothe and open our bodies and minds to more love and peace.

I became fascinated with the pain. It was like saying "Yes, you are here. I am curious," because making the pain wrong and trying hard to get it to go away, created more emotional pain.

With an open mind and heart, learning to demand nothing, we can observe sensations of discomfort, tightness, stiffness, heat, coolness, denseness, and the spaciousness around it. The emotions of frustration, anger, sadness, fear and anxiety can be witnessed as well without collapsing into them and sometimes sensing and detecting their intensity in the body. By observing and embracing them and mindfully questioning their presence, we can learn much about ourselves. We can begin to find our soul's journey with pain. From this place of fascination, we find the lessons behind the pain more interesting than anything outside ourselves.

Pain teaches us many things.

Pain is a reminder that we are human and alive.
Pain is a reminder that something needs attention and care.
Pain is a reminder to slow down, stop "doing" and start "being" present.
Pain is a reminder to surrender and accept the moment.
Pain is a reminder to go within and bring comfort.
Pain is a reminder to investigate and listen deeply.
Pain is a reminder to relax and nurture.
Pain is a reminder to shift our thinking.
Pain is a reminder to love our self.
Pain is a reminder to speak up for our needs.
Pain is a reminder to have compassion.
Pain is a reminder to embrace our emotions, without blame.

Pain is a reminder to massage and touch our bodies with love. Pain is a reminder to connect authentically with our self and others. Pain is a reminder to make our bodies and our inner sanctuary a priority.

Every pain has its own light and is a gift that belongs. Around and through all pain is a crack where light can come in and lessons can be learned. If we remember this, even if for a second, we are increasing the energetic awareness of love for ourselves and for the world. This choice always lies within us. Physically, we can love our pain and listen as we take the next step. Mentally, we can change our thinking and identify our negative thoughts remembering they are just passing through. Emotionally, we can embrace our uncomfortable feelings knowing they are but energy releasing and then find our hearts' desire behind those emotions. The more we get out of the way and surrender to the light within pain, life's perfection reveals itself. Everything has its place, even pain.

FINDING THE GIFT IN PAIN - PRACTICES

Do one practice a day.
If you enjoy it, circle the practice and
add it to your wellness tool box.

DAY 1 PRACTICE
Embracing and Saying "Yes" to Pain

Sometimes we make pain wrong. We say "No, not this; this shouldn't be happening to me," or "I want this pain to go away. Be gone, now!"

By saying "yes" to pain, we connect to pain in a new way. Instead of trying to make the pain go away or trying to fix the pain, we are willing to get to know the pain and perhaps learn something new about our self.

When physical pain or illness arises with intensity, practice saying "yes" to the sensations and lovingly accept what is. If emotional pain, such as anxiety, anger, frustration or loneliness arise along with the physical pain, saying "yes" to the emotion with a soft energetic embrace can shift everything. If there is resistance, practice saying "yes" to the resistance.

Sometimes, the idea of saying "yes" to pain may bring up fear. A common belief is that by saying "Yes pain, I accept you," the pain may stay or get worse. Not so. When saying "yes" to pain, we let go of wanting or expecting anything from it. By saying "yes," we simply are willing to accept and honor what is. It is as if we are being a friend to the pain, giving it loving attention. By doing this, we can listen with compassion and eventually hear what the pain may or may not need as well as what it may have to teach us.

1. *Begin by locating a physical tight spot or pain in your body. Say "yes" to the sensations and/or pain in your body. How do you feel when you do this?*

    _____

    _____

    _____

2. *If there is an uncomfortable emotion that rises such as anger or resistance, say "yes" to this too. What do you experience when you do this?*

    _____

    _____

    _____

3. *Focus on your breath and say "yes" again to the sensations and/or pain. Notice your breath and imagine your breath softly surrounding and penetrating the sensation in your body. Again, gently say "yes" to whatever is happening. How do you feel now?*

    _____

    _____

    _____

4. *Do this for several minutes. How does your body feel? How is your body responding? How is the pain responding?*

    _____

    _____

    _____

Use this as a daily practice and notice if the pain or tension becomes easier to embrace.

DAY 2 PRACTICE
Presence to Tension, Physical Sensations and Pain

1. *Begin by locating a tight sensation/pain in one specific area in the body. Example: center of the forehead, upper chest, right hip, left side of the neck under the jaw line. (If there are many sensations, choose the one that is the most intense or whichever one grabs your attention first.) Focus on that sensation.*

2. *On a scale of one to ten, rate your tightness or pain and its intensity. One being a mild sensation and ten being the most intense, almost unbearable pain. What number would you give the sensation you are focusing on? ____*

3. *Take your time and ask yourself these questions, pausing between each one. How big is the pain? ____ Size of a quarter? ____ A brick? ____ How long is it? ____ An inch long? ____ Foot long? ____ Can you find any solid boundaries around the sensations? ____ If so, do those boundaries keep shifting? ____ Or are they stationary? ____ Can you name where the boundaries are? ____ Does the sensation feel solid like a wall? ____ Or more like a sponge? ____ Is it dense like cement? ____ Or dense like sand? ____ Is it sharp like a pointed knife? ____ Or dull like a finger? ____ Is it moving? ____ Or more stagnant? ____*

4. *After the investigation, check in to see if its intensity has shifted. How would you rate it now? ____ (Rate it on a scale of 1 to 10.)*

5. *Be present with the sensations for a while and begin to visualize soothing, energetic, loving kindness around the remaining sensations (pain). See if the sensations want a light hug, tight squeeze, firm massage or just empathy. Bring an open, curious mind to the sensations (pain).*

What will nurture it the most? Give the sensations what it is needing for a few minutes.

_____

_____

_____

_____

6. *Check in to see if its intensity has shifted. How would you rate it now? _____ (Rate it on a scale of 1 to 10.)*

Repeat this activity for as long as you enjoy.

DAY 3 PRACTICE
What Does This Pain Need?

The following questions are to assist you in getting clarity on what will help you deal with pain and to discover what your specific pain may need. Ask these questions and then wait for a "yes" or "no" to pop in. You can also practice kinesthetic testing (More in of this in Chapter VII: Inner Inquiry Questions). If you feel a slight expansion in the body after you ask the question, your body is saying "yes." If you feel any contraction after asking a question, the answer is "no." Make sure to pause between each question as you wait for the answer.

SELF-HEALING QUESTIONS

Is this pain manageable? _____ Does it want me to comfort it? _____ Am I needing to slow down and nurture myself? _____ Do I need to stop, and sit with the pain so I can receive healing energy? _____ Does the pain want gentle touch? _____ Does it desire deep physical manipulation and massage? _____ Is this pain needing movement and *stretching? _____ Do I need to be still and breathe into the pain? _____ Would I enjoy listening to soothing, healing music? _____ Do I need to change my attitude about the pain? _____ Shall I call a friend? _____ Shall I look online for more information? _____ Shall I search online for natural ointments and methods of healing? _____ Do I need to ignore it and get to it later when I'm in a safe, comforting space? _____*

ENVIRONMENTAL CHANGE QUESTIONS

Am I needing change in my environment? _____ In my home environment? _____ With my job? _____ Do I need to identify my needs at work? _____ At home? _____ Do I need to ask for my needs to be met in any relationship? _____ Do I need to change something in my diet? _____ Add to my diet? _____ Take something out of my diet? _____ Adjust my exercise routine? _____ Add more stretching? _____ Do I need more leisure/play time? _____ More time in nature? _____ More quiet time? _____ Do I need to let go of a relationship? _____ Is there a healing group or class that would be wise for me to attend? _____

CARE FROM SPECIALISTS, DOCTORS AND MEDICINE

Am I needing extra help, more than my environment can give me? _____ Do I need to see my primary care doctor? _____ Do I need to see a chiropractor? _____ Physical therapist? _____ Acupuncturist? _____ Naturopathic doctor? _____ Massage therapist? _____ Do I need an herbal remedy? _____ Do I need medication? _____ Shall I call a counselor or life coach? _____ Is there another specialist or friend that might assist me? _____

Chapter 3

AFFIRMATIONS AS TRUTH REMINDERS

*"It's not what happens but how we perceive
what happens that determines our experiences."*

VALERIE JOI FIDDMONT

THE PAIN IN MY TEETH AND MOUTH CAUSED A GREAT DEAL OF tension in my jaw, head and neck. Many fears arose along side the pain. The doctors, with all their diagnoses and suggestions, were well intentioned, but it was overwhelming. There weren't any clear solutions regarding my situation and there were so many different opinions. Orthognathic surgery was the last thing I wanted. And "chronic" pain, well who wants that? At least I was clear that 16 caps on my teeth wasn't the answer and I didn't need orthodontics either. Sitting with hours of pain on and off throughout the day, my mind chattered obsessively with fearful thoughts.

I am afraid of being in pain all the time. I am so tired. What if I'm unable to function and lose my job? I am afraid of being alone and not having friends. I am afraid to surrender and let go. I am afraid of the western medical system and scared that the doctors won't listen to me or consider my needs. My life should be different than this. I'm not lovable anymore. I have nothing to offer anyone because of this pain. I don't want to be a burden or downer around others. What a waste of my time, my money and my life.

There were times my negative thoughts wouldn't stop.
I couldn't turn them off, no matter how hard
I tried. So I watched them as they ran amuck
and sadness and fear were close behind.

I wanted my teeth, neck and jaw to be different than they were. I wanted my situation to be different than it was. But wanting something other than what actually was, only brought frustration. I was not in control. Depression lurked at the edges as I sat with the constant pain. I knew I didn't want to go down that gray hole, so my pity party didn't last long. I pulled out some of my favorite affirmations from a couple great books, *You Can Heal Your Life* and *A Course in Miracles* (Hayes, 1987; Schucman, 1972) that had remained with me over the years. They were the best affirmation books I had ever come across. I recalled some of my favorites and modified them to fit my situation as I was preparing for yet another root canal.

"I can relax. I am safe in the hands of this doctor.
I trust my intuition and life's flow."
I took a few deep breaths.
My resistance began to soften.

Life's challenges come in many forms and most of us don't initially welcome those challenges completely. I know I didn't. Sometimes we get angry, frustrated and anxious during challenging times. Being reminded of our true essence of love and of what is really important in life is what supports us while going over the bumps, lumps and stumps in our paths. We are seldom in control of our surroundings or the experiences that come our way. However, we can choose what thoughts we want to hold about ourselves, our experiences and those around us.

Affirmations remind us who we are in the midst of life and its challenging circumstances. They are reminders of that which is already true about oneself, others and life in general. Affirmations are not about trying to make the situation or pain go away. But rather, affirmations are truth reminders that keep our spirits high and our hearts open.

Positive self-talk and affirmations are also stepping stones to helping one break free from old, conditioned and fearful mental patterns about pain and difficult situations. When we change our perspective, our emotions and attitudes change too. When this shift happens, we can open again and learn our lessons and find peace and meaning in challenging experiences.

While sitting in my car before going in to a doctor's appointment for my root canal, I wondered, *Are these root canals really worth it? The tooth that was just pulled had one and it lasted less than a year. The other two root canals I had were fine.* Anxiety set in. *How could I question the doctor without making him think I was being disrespectful of his knowledge and authority?* I really liked Dr. Geminiz. *But what do I know?* I laid back in my car, repeating my affirmations to calm my nerves. *I am safe. I speak my truth with ease.* I felt uncomfortable speaking up to authority figures. An observation came to me. *I guess it's because I think they have more knowledge than I do and wouldn't listen to my intuition about my own body.* My insecurities and conditioned beliefs that the doctors know more about my body than I do were very deeply ingrained. *Old programming, I guess.* I sighed and decided to shift some of the old patterned thoughts. *Dr. Geminiz is on my side. I can trust myself. I will know what to say.* The anxiety lessened but was still there. I sank back into the car seat and began repeating in my mind.

I am safe. I can relax. It is safe to speak
my truth and ask questions.
The more I felt the truth of these
statements, the more I could feel my
inner confidence strengthening.

I got out of the car and went into his office. His assistant took me into one of the rooms where I sat and waited for Dr. Geminiz. As I waited, I took deep, relaxing breaths and continued the Truth reminders. *I can trust myself. It is safe to ask questions. I can relax now.* The doctor entered the room. I greeted him calmly. "Hello Dr. Geminiz."

"Well hello to you. Sorry to hear about yet another tooth."

I centered myself as my concerns arose. "Dr. Geminiz. Umm, what if this root canal doesn't work? I mean, I feel like I might be wasting my money again. The other root canal only lasted a year and I had to get it pulled in the end. I mean, what do you think?" I stumbled through my words.

He replied, "Well we want to do the least aggressive procedures first and a root canal is better than getting a tooth pulled. We want to do anything we can to save that tooth."

"But I don't want to lose more money if it doesn't work, like the last one. That root canal only lasted for a year and then it was pulled." I reiterated.

"There is a very minimal percentage of root canals that fail. Let's hope for the best."

I ended up having the root canal and felt good about working through my fears of speaking up and shifting that old conditioning about doctor's authority. I still wasn't sure about the root canal, but it sounded as if it was protocol. *The doctor did say "least aggressive procedures first," and root canals are better than pulling teeth.*

I used many affirmations, some for the physical pain, some for my fears and others for my negative thoughts. *I trust this moment and surrender my fears. I move forward with grace and ease.* Affirmations such as these got me through the challenging moments. I still had pain in several other areas in my back molars and was dealing with the unknown of jaw surgery. The affirmations gave me acceptance and love for my body, soothed the pain and supported me in accepting that this pain was part of my unique soul's journey.

AFFIRMATIONS AS TRUTH REMINDERS FOR PHYSICAL, EMOTIONAL AND MENTAL WELL-BEING

I had never experienced this much constant physical pain, day in and day out. Affirmations helped me to embrace the experience and love myself unconditionally.

My resistance to the pain lessened and I learned to accept the pain and my body, always doing my best to listen to the pain. I learned to talk to the pain. I learned to be present with it and ask my body what it needed.

FOR PHYSICAL PAIN
Self-Loving Affirmations

1. *Even though I have painful, sensations in my body, I accept and love myself.*

2. *Even though I have pain in my _____ (name a part of your body), I completely love and accept it as it is.*

3. *I am willing to treat this pain as I would a good friend. You are welcomed and loved.*

4. *This situation, this challenge, this illness does not have meaning, other than the meaning I give to it.*

Anger, sadness, depression, and loneliness were a big part of my experience. I realized that emotional pain was similar to physical pain. Embracing my "negative" emotions was important.

If I didn't, negative emotions could impact both my physical and emotional well-being. I needed to give myself permission to sit with these deeper emotions and fears and become curious about them; otherwise, depression would begin to set in. In my deep looking, I discovered a whole range of emotions. I found when the emotions were accepted and allowed to be expressed in a healthy way, healing occurred and my heart opened.

FOR EMOTIONAL PAIN
Self-Loving Affirmations

1. *I accept all feelings that arise; anger, sadness and fear are welcomed.*

2. *I hold sweet space around my emotions. It is safe to feel.*

3. *I am willing to be present with my anger and listen to what it is telling me.*

4. *I am grateful to be human and experience all emotions as my own without projecting them on to others.*

I needed to address the thought patterns in my mind
that wanted to make my situation wrong.
This shouldn't be happening to me.
Life shouldn't be this way.

There were many thoughts of blame and judgment toward the doctors and health care system too. Using affirmations however, I was able to become self-empowered. I was able to see through and let go of negative mental activity. This helped me stay uplifted; so I could focus on the situation, to ask what the lessons were here to teach me and to see what needed to be done.

FOR NEGATIVE THOUGHT PATTERNS
Self Loving Affirmations

1. *There is no real conflict here. It is only in my mind. I choose peace.*

2. *I let go of negative, fear-based thoughts and desired outcomes and affirm that there is only love here.*

3. *I choose loving, gentle thoughts for myself and others because those thoughts feel good.*

4. *I am willing to see things differently. I am willing to be with this situation to learn and grow.*

Guilt came up, because I had to make myself the priority above all else. This brought up some of my deep hidden co-dependent belief patterns.

I had no energy to help my friends, family or community. I had concerns of being a burden on others. And since my ability to give to others was little to nothing, because of the pain, I had the opportunity to face those old belief systems and habits. Codependent habits of making others a greater priority than my own well-being were dropping away, and knowing my true inner worth and trusting my inner wisdom were coming to the forefront.

FOR CO-DEPENDENT/PEOPLE PLEASING
Self Loving Affirmations

1. *It is okay to say "no" to others and make my Self and inner joy my first priority.*

2. *I am not here to fix or save anyone. I let go of feeling respon-*

sible for others (over the age of 18 if you have children) and the happiness of others.

3. *It doesn't matter what anyone thinks of me. I speak my truth with love, honesty and clarity.*

4. *With love and ease, I let go of relationships that no longer support my inner growth.*

I couldn't push, force or hurry this healing process along. When I tried to make my healing happen faster than it wanted to go, it would only create more pain, emotionally, mentally and physically.

I was used to getting things done in a "timely" manner and so I placed those beliefs on this situation as well. The challenge with my teeth however made me face this old behavior and belief. This situation called for another way of being. Patience, surrendering, being mindful, listening and trusting the process were my lessons.

FOR TRUSTING THE HEALING PROCESS
Self Loving Affirmations

1. *Healing energy is constantly moving through me. I accept the perfect timing of my healing.*

2. *I am patient with the process of healing. I take as much time as my emotions, my body and my mind needs.*

3. *I trust that I will always be taken care of. I have all I need in this very moment.*

4. *It is safe to relax as I listen and wait for clarity for my next step on this healing journey.*

**I experienced a great deal of fear and anxiety around
speaking up for my needs to the doctors.
My intuition was often telling me something different
than what they were saying.**

I had a belief that doctors were somehow superior with all their
knowledge and that they should know what my problem is and
how to fix it. Trusting my inner knowing beyond the authorities
and advocating for my needs felt overwhelming. I was afraid they
wouldn't work with me. Not until I could give myself empathy,
could I give them the same. Affirmations helped me keep things
in perspective and to come back to a centered, positive place so I
could work with the doctors.

FOR TRUSTING MYSELF AND OTHERS
Self Loving Affirmations

1. *I trust my inner wisdom and will be guided to the perfect
   doctors/healers and healing practices.*

2. *I listen to my intuition and its guidance before all others.*

3. *My Higher Self connects to the doctor's Higher Self. All is in
   perfect order. I let go of fear and choose to trust.*

4. *I let go of fear and control, and trust the perfect outcome
   of this situation. I receive the gifts of healing, physically,
   emotionally, mentally and spiritually with this doctor/
   person/situation.*

**Remembering my true essence beyond this
experience helped me embrace my journey
and stay out of depression.**

I am more than the pain, more than my body, I am a soul on a fasci-

AFFIRMATIONS AS TRUTH REMINDERS

nating journey. These reminders helped me tap into the universal love that runs through me and through everything. The following affirmations were invaluable truths that reminded me that life is about learning the deeper lessons of love and staying connected to my Self.

TRUE ESSENCE BEYOND THE SITUATION
Self Loving Affirmations

1. *I am connected to unconditional love beyond all appearances. Nothing can harm my true essence.*

2. *This experience is as it is supposed to be. I accept all aspects of my soul's journey.*

3. *I am Love beyond this form, this body and beyond this situation.*

4. *This situation too shall pass. My body is temporary. My true essence is eternal. I choose love in every moment.*

These were some of the greatest reminders and affirmations I used during this trying time. You can create your own personal affirmations and truth reminders, ones that directly affect your unique soul's journey. When creating an affirmation, remember that these reminders are NOT about changing a person or your external world, but claiming the truth of your inner being and inner world. Create affirmations that bring you the greatest amount of truth, clarity and joy. Here are some general guidelines and ideas in creating your own affirmations.

1. **Make affirmations in the present tense. Claim your truth boldly, with clarity, focus and commitment.** "I know what to do in every moment" instead of "I hope I will know what to do in the next moment." (Johnson, 2002).

2. **if there is fear or resistance to your affirmation when you say, try beginning with "I am willing to...".** This preface is a softer approach until we are completely ready to let go of an old behavior. "I am willing to let go of the belief that this shouldn't be happening. I am willing to see this differently."

3. **An affirmation can also be used as a DENIAL, denying or rejecting any negative thoughts and stories we tell ourselves.** "I do NOT believe my negative thoughts" or "these thoughts have NO hold on me!" or "This thought is simply NOT true." Eventually, you will simply ignore the negative ones.

4. **Begin with "I have always..." to erase the power of the past and focus on this moment.** "I have always trusted that I am taken care of," or "I have always listened to my inner guidance first and made myself a priority." When you claim your truth right now, it wipes out all of the past and boldly proclaims your commitment!

Try different affirmations and see which ones works for you. There is no "right" way to do them. Whatever affirmations get you out of negative thinking patterns; helps you remember who you are or help you accept your challenges in a positive light are the ones to use. Be creative and have fun. Post them up in your bedroom or refrigerator. After saying them, see how they feel in your body and how they affect your emotions. You may have resistance at first as you shift out of old patterns. Be patient as you integrate the affirmations and new behaviors that come with your new way of seeing and moving through life.

AFFIRMATIONS AS TRUTH REMINDERS - PRACTICES

Do one practice a day.
If you enjoy it, circle the practice and
add it to your wellness tool box.

DAY 1 PRACTICE
Affirmations and Your Emotional Health

This practice is two-fold. It will give you a visceral experience of seeing the difference between negative thoughts and positive thoughts; and how each affects your emotions. This practice also will help you identify any unconscious thoughts you might be saying to yourself and help shift them.

1. *Experiencing the Difference Between Negative and Positive Thoughts*

   a. *Say a NEGATIVE thought out loud to yourself. "I'm not lovable and never have been." Pause for a while and notice what goes on in your body and emotions. How would you describe your body's sensations and emotions after you say that thought?*

   _____

   _____

   b. *Now affirm what is actually true, using a POSITIVE affirmation. "I'm totally lovable and always have been." Again, notice what emotions rise and what physical sensations come up. How would you describe them?*

_____

_____

c. *Now try this NEGATIVE thought. "They should have known better." Pause and observe the sensations in and around your heart and body. Notice how you feel emotionally. Describe how your heart feels.*

_____

_____

d. *Now affirm this POSITIVE reminder. "They are learning and are human. They are doing the best they can with the consciousness they have." Again, check in with your body and overall energy vibe. How do you feel?*

_____

_____

e. *Can you see how thoughts affect your body and emotions?*

_____

2. **Identifying Unconscious Negative Thoughts and Shifting Them into Positive Thoughts**

a. *Now identify any negative unconscious thought patterns that you say about yourself. Examples: "I'm not good enough. I should have accomplished more. I'm not lovable. Something is wrong with me. Why do things always happen to me?" Dive deep into your unconscious beliefs about yourself, your body and your life.*

Write down your old NEGATIVE thought patterns about yourself, your body and your life.

_____

_____

_____

_____

_____

_____

_____

b. *Shift those thoughts into positive affirmations. Write down the new POSITIVE affirmations about yourself, your body and your life.*

_____

_____

_____

_____

_____

c. *Are there any other negative unconscious thought patterns that you say about others: your children, family and friends? Examples: "They should be different. People are not trustworthy. I can't trust men/women."*

Write down your old NEGATIVE thought patterns about others.

_____

_____

_____

_____

_____

d. Write down your new POSITIVE affirmations about others.

Throughout your day, when negative thought patterns arise, simply replace them with your new positive affirmations. Make this a daily practice and see how quickly you can identify and replace any thoughts that don't make you feel good. Watch how your emotions shift.

DAY 2 PRACTICE
Creating Daily Affirmations

In this practice, you will create your own personalized daily affirmations. After doing so, place your personalized affirmations next to your bed, on your mirror, in your car or on your refrigerator; wherever you can see them. Say your positive reminders to yourself every morning before you start your day and see how they change your outlook and emotional well-being.

Examples of Affirmations as Truth Reminders

1. *I am open to receiving all the good in my day.*

2. *I take the time to own and explore my reactions, triggers*

and negative emotions today without blaming others.

3. *I speak up for my needs in a loving way.*

4. *It is safe to relax, feel and be in my body.*

5. *Self-love is a spiritual practice; I make myself a priority throughout my day.*

Now write down any affirmations that spoke to you above, or create your own positive reminders. If you don't know where to begin, start with "I" followed by a verb in the present tense.

1. ....

2. ....

3. ....

Affirmations may change depending on your needs. Only you will know which ones will affect you and empower you the most.

DAY 3 PRACTICE
Healing Mind-Body Affirmations

Within the cells of our bodies, we hold unresolved emotions and beliefs from the past. As we learn to become more present in our bodies, unconscious beliefs and emotions can often rise to the surface. Affirmations can help shift subconscious mental patterns and help heal the heart, mind and body. They can reach deep into places where we carry pain and dis-ease.

Here are several healing mind-body affirmations adapted from "You Can Heal Your Life" by Louise Hay. Think about where you often carry aches and tension in your body. Circle the body part and AFFIRMATION you can relate to.

EARS – PROBLEM: *Arguing with others. Not able to listen to other's needs and communicate your needs with love.*
AFFIRMATION: *"I listen for deeper truths, needs and desires. I am in harmony with the heart of all beings and living things."*

SHOULDERS – PROBLEM: *Carrying other's burdens. Being a martyr and codependent. Shouldering others' responsibilities.*
AFFIRMATION: *"I let go of feeling responsible for other's experiences. Instead, I focus on my own lessons and trust the universe will take care of others."*

HANDS – PROBLEM: *Grasping with fear and control. Trying harder than needed. Handling more than is yours to manage.*
AFFIRMATION: *I let go and handle life with joy. I bend and create with ease from a place of balance as I center from within.*

HEART – PROBLEM: *Forgetting about the joy in life because of fear and the focus on money. Lack of self-love and compassion for others.*
AFFIRMATION: *"I choose that which brings me joy. I set boundaries easily and say 'no' to that which does not. I open my heart with compassion and for deeper understanding."*

STOMACH – PROBLEM: *Fear of change and resistance to digesting new ideas.*
AFFIRMATION: *"I flow with life. I receive all of life's experiences. I take time to digest and integrate life's lessons as they come."*

LOWER BACK – PROBLEM: *Not feeling supported in life. Exerting too much effort through the way of force and pushiness. Not trusting the flow of life.*
AFFIRMATION: *"I let go of fear and control. I trust and surrender to life's divine timing and unfoldment. Life supports me and I can relax.*

FEET – PROBLEM: *Not being grounded or present in life.*
AFFIRMATION: *"I stand with confidence. I pause and become present as I listen and move mindfully. I am connected and in harmony with my body and the earth."*

Check out "Health and Well-Being Resources" at the end of the book for more Affirmation information for diseases and ailments in "You Can Heal Your Life" by Louise Hayes.

Chapter 4

THOUGHTS, EMOTIONS, PHYSICAL SENSATIONS AND THEIR INTERCONNECTEDNESS

"There's a lot we can do in the fast lane.
We can grow and we can expand.
But we cannot deepen, and we cannot integrate
our experiences, unless we slow down."

ANGELES ARRIEN

IT HAD BEEN MONTHS SINCE THE PLACEMENT OF MY IMPLANT and the pulsating pain in it did not go away. In fact, the constant throbbing around the base of the implant was now creating tightness in my forehead. I called Dr. Black, the oral surgeon who had done the procedure, to ask about the situation. I told him about the throbbing irritation and that I sensed the implant would need to be pulled. He insisted that I was experiencing nerve pain and explained that I would have pain whether I had the implant removed or not.

The pain wasn't going away and I had had enough. Frustration and anger stirred. I wasn't buying Dr. Black's reasoning. I laid quietly observing the emotional frustration and the physical tightness in my neck. Eventually my emotions settled.

As I acknowledged the emotion, the tightness in my neck softened. I was amazed at the interconnectedness of my emotions and my body.

Only after dealing with my emotions could I hear my inner Self. I began asking simple "yes" or "no" questions. *Does this implant need to be removed?* My body expanded slightly when the answer was "yes," and my body energetically became weak and contracted when the answer was "no." My intuition said "yes." I needed the implant to be extracted and I trusted my body and the answers I received.

The next day, I called my dentist, Dr. Par, for support. I told him about the constant pain in the implant and that I thought it needed to be pulled. He recommended I go see Dr. Gregory, another oral surgeon, for a second opinion. He gave Dr. Gregory a very high recommendation, saying he was at the top of his field and well-respected in the dentistry community.

The next week, I was driving to Dr. Gregory's office for a consultation. I felt agitated and scattered as I watched negative thoughts start up. The thoughts were persistent this time and were stronger than the day before. *Dr. Black and Dr. Gregory probably talked about my situation and are in cahoots working against me. After all, they are colleagues.* Fear arose. *What if Dr. Gregory doesn't believe me either about the pain in my implant?* I pulled out my Inner Physician toolbox. *These thoughts will not have the best of me!* I affirmed. I focused on the sensations in my body so I wouldn't attach or believe all the negative thoughts. When I shifted my focus toward the intense sensations (pain), the negative thoughts had no attention and therefore lost their power.

Every thought creates a nerve impulse that is sent from the brain, moves down the spinal column and makes its way to various parts of the body. Stress and negative thoughts in our minds that are not addressed in healthy ways become toxic to our lives, our relationships and our bodies. Staying mindful of negative thoughts and shifting them or not attaching to (believing in) them helps calm our negative emotions and in turn, the nervous system. We can learn to observe our negative thoughts and remind ourselves to stay in the present moment. That way, we do not create toxicity in our lives.

**It was difficult work not to blame Dr. Black.
The negative thoughts were definitely there. But if
I gave into them, I knew the outcome would
cause more angst, more drama and upset
for myself and those around me.**

So I chose to keep my focus on the sensations that were rising in my body. This helped me stay present. Eventually my body began to relax and soften and the negative thoughts were gone. *Ahhhh, peace again.* Once my body and mind relaxed, compassionate thoughts for Dr. Black rolled through. *He is human. We all make mistakes. The universe knows what's for my highest good.*

**Just as my negative thoughts had created tightness in
my body, the compassionate thoughts helped
my heart soften and my body relax.**

I pulled up and parked in front of Dr. Gregory's office. I sat in my car, tilted my chair back and relaxed my neck and mouth for several minutes. This grounded me and helped me gather as much positive energy as I could before entering Dr. Gregory's office. Dealing with the unknown, so many different personalities and opinions from the doctors meant a lot of self-soothing. Anxiety was right around the corner.

When I walked through the door, I greeted the receptionist with a smile. We exchanged a few words. I filled out some paperwork and she directed me to the next room. I sat down in the surgical chair and was grateful to have more time to relax and center before Dr. Gregory came in.

Within minutes he came in with a pleasant demeanor. He sat down on a little black stool, perched like an attentive bird. "Hi Gerilyn. I see you are having some pain around your left, upper implant." He said as he looked at my chart.

"Yes, it's been there for months." My body relaxed a little as I could feel his caring presence.

"Well, the x-rays don't show anything particular. It actually looks strong and stable." He pointed to the x-ray. "Can I look inside?" I opened my mouth. He probed and wiggled the implant a little.

"Ouch," I winced.

«We definitely don't want you to be in pain. And sometimes we don't always know the cause of pain. Your bone on the upper jaw line is thinner than the bone on the lower. So if you were to get it removed, I wouldn't advise you to get another one in its place."

"If the pain would stop, it would be worth having the implant removed," I said. "It cost me a lot to have it put in, but I'm tired of dealing with the pain." I could tell by his words, his presence and attentiveness that he was on my side. I felt relieved. "I have other pain going on with a couple other molars too," I added.

"Well, let's deal with this one first," he replied. "You know you can get reimbursed for a failed implant?"

"Really?"

"Yes," he continued and explained the details.

"I did not know that. Thank you Dr. Gregory. That information is very helpful."

I left his office hopeful and eager to call Dr. Black.

After resting my jaw and neck in the car, I called Dr. Black immediately and set up an appointment. His assistants were able to get me in the very next day.

I was on time as I arrived for my appointment. This was my third visit to see Dr. Black about the situation and I was feeling nervous. His assistant ushered me into his office and took some more x-rays of the implant. He walked in several minutes later. "Hi Gerilyn, how are you?" There were x-rays where he was standing.

"Not very well. The pain is still there around my implant." I raised my eyebrows with disappointment.

He pointed to the screen where I could see my implant on the x-ray. "The x-rays show no signs of inflammation or infection. Everything is fine."

"But there is pain around it," I insisted.

"It's often the nerves that are affecting the area and that may well be for the rest of your life," Dr. Black explained.

"I don't know what is going on, but I'm tired of this pain. I'm wondering if…" He must have been reading my mind as I was about to ask for the removal of the implant.

"Extracting it won't necessarily help. I suggest that you take pain medication that I can prescribe."

I spoke up quickly, with tears welling up. "I don't want to take medication for the rest of my life."

"Well sometimes that's what is needed," Dr. Black responded.

"Don't other people ever report sensitivity to implants? Maybe it's the metal?" I suggested with frustration.

He insisted. "No, no, that is very unlikely and extremely rare." He explained the type of metal they use and why that couldn't be the problem.

I sat there as I noticed the pain around the implant. "Don't you care I'm in pain?"

"Of course I do," he responded.

I didn't believe him. "Well, Dr. Gregory told me I could get a reimbursement for a failed implant. I'm thinking it would be best to get it removed."

Dr. Black became irritated with me. He abruptly moved some items on the counter. "We've done all we can. If you choose to get it extracted, I suggest you go to Dr. Gregory," he said gruffly.

"I'm just trying to find a solution; I don't want to be in pain anymore."

"Listen Gerilyn, I will reimburse you fully, if, after it is removed, there is no pain. I don't however, think that is the problem."

I left his office and sat in my car frozen with fear. I had just confronted a doctor who seemed as if he knew more than I did about what was going on in my body. My inner authority felt strong and I comforted myself by lying back in the car, placing a pillow under my head and attempting to relax my body. I watched anger rise and the thoughts that followed. *Doesn't he know how sensitive I am and how much his inconsiderate way of addressing me affects me? These procedures have been difficult enough. I don't deserve this.*

**I placed my hands behind my head to
nurture the pain as I continued to
observe my thoughts and anger.**

Dr. Black has a lack of integrity. Why isn't he pulling it? He's sending me to Dr. Gregory instead of finishing what he started. This man who was my angel started acting like anything but. *If it wasn't for Dr. Gregory, I wouldn't have even known I could get my money back. But NO, Dr. Black... he didn't divulge that. He's a jerk.* I felt angry. There wasn't much I could do though. It was Dr. Black's office and *he's the doctor.*

I paused for a moment and noticed how crappy I felt and then recognized all the negative thoughts. I then recalled the wisdom I had gained from studying with Dr. William Glasser and reading his book, *Choice Theory*. He used the metaphor of a car. The front wheels are thoughts and emotions and the back wheels are the body and actions. *Don't let your thoughts and emotions run the car.* I began to ask some simple questions I had learned from his workshops on the basic needs/desires/wants. (Glasser, 2001)

What am I wanting?
Is what I am thinking getting me what I truly desire?

My anger pointed to the fact that I desired an empathetic doctor who was willing to work with me, one with integrity. *Yes, those are the things I wanted… empathy, collaboration and integrity.* Dr. Black wasn't meeting my needs. I gave myself empathy. *You deserve doctors who listen to you and know what is right for you. You deserve doctors with integrity and those that follow through.* That felt good. My heart started to soften and compassion for him came up. *Dr. Black did pull my tooth during his lunch break when I needed urgent help. And, he is human,* I told myself. *And for whatever reason, the implant is not working.*

It's time for a new oral surgeon who will listen to me and who has integrity. I told myself. I liked Dr. Gregory and he came highly recommended. *I'll set up an appointment to see him again.*

I called Dr. Gregory's office. I was ready for the removal of the failed implant. We set up an appointment for the following week. My belly was in knots. I was scared even thinking about going through another invasive surgery around this implant. And yet, I knew the removal of it needed to be done. After validating my emotions, I looked for my deeper need. I wanted to be in control but I wasn't. I couldn't be in control of anything but my own reactions. I worked on having positive thoughts. *I have hope. Dr. Gregory will extract this failed implant and I'll get my money back from Dr. Black. I trust my intuition. The pain will soon be gone!*

The next week, Dr. Gregory removed the implant. Afterwards, I drove home and went to my room, took penicillin and laid on my bed snuggling with my soft pillow. The pain was almost instantaneously gone! I called Dr. Black and told him the pain was gone. Dr. Black said I needed to wait a few months to make sure the pain didn't come back again before he was willing to reimburse me. *I can wait a few months.* I knew the pain wasn't coming back!

Later that evening I had some sadness about losing a tooth and the failed implant. I knew that if I didn't acknowledge these deeper emotions, they would stack up, pressure would build inside and depression could overtake me. If I suppressed my negative emotions, more tightness in my chest and abdomen would occur, creating even more physical discomfort.

As I became present with the hidden emotions, I would remind myself, *it is safe to feel.* Tears fell, tears of grief. It was as if I was grieving the death of my teeth. The tears came and went. The aggressive procedures and difficulty with Dr. Black took their toll on my body and nervous system. I nurtured and comforted myself with loving presence until I felt calm, loved and restored.

I had an old childhood wound.
I could hear my mother saying, "don't cry."

When I was growing up, tears and emotions weren't always validated in my family. In fact, sometimes crying and showing emotions were made wrong. I had addressed this emotional wound many times. It took me years to undo the beliefs held about expressing negative emotions, like anger and sadness. I had heard someone once say "Tears water the earth and open hearts."

I affirmed to myself,
yes, I am watering the earth with my tears.
It is safe to feel.

Most of us have repressed emotions from hearing things like, "Don't cry. Suck it up. Be strong. Crying is for babies. Come on, be happy," or "If you keep crying, I'll give you something to cry about." Our society and families have passed these dysfunctional beliefs and unconscious ways of suppressing negative emotions on to us. It is not done on purpose though. They wanted us to "be happy" or wanted us to experience peace and harmony. Parents or perhaps other adults in our lives may have given us rewards or scolded us with punitive consequences so we wouldn't feel the difficult emotions that were rising within us. As a result of this suppression, we store these emotions and beliefs in our bodies.

Unfortunately, these unconscious emotions and habits can eventually lead us to disease, illness or unhealthy ways of relating to ourselves and others. Turning towards emotional pain and embracing it is a foreign idea to many of us. Identifying negative emotions, expressing them and asking for one's needs in a healthy way may be an uncomfortable edge, especially in close relationships.

One day after work, I went to see my primary care doctor to discuss the possibility of applying for disability because of the pain I was experiencing. They gave me a blood test. I don't like needles and the nurse had to do the procedure twice because she didn't take enough blood the first time. *Ouch!* I called a friend to tell her of my situation. I was extremely tired, my jaw and teeth were aching and my temples were pounding. I was trying to stay positive in my thinking. "Wow, I made it through a blood test, needles and all. I'm grateful!" I exclaimed. "Glad it's over though!" I was trying to lift myself out of the pain. It was a tough day and I was glad my negative thoughts or emotions hadn't spilled over onto anyone.

My friend sensed something more was
happening and gingerly inquired,
"How are you really feeling about all of this?
I'm sensing some sadness."

My friend and I had created a relationship in which we honored our emotions. She was someone who was emotionally safe for me. Tears began rolling down my face and on to the phone.

"It's okay to cry," she said.

More tears streamed down. "Thank you. I've been trying to be so strong. I don't know how I'm going to get through this. This is really hard on my body." She listened and validated my fears and tears. I could feel her presence. She was not trying to fix or change me. She was just there to listen.

What seemed like an hour was actually
probably five minutes. I released deep,

**suppressed emotions that I had been
carrying for a couple of weeks.**

After the release, it felt as if something had moved through me and lifted off my chest. My heart felt nurtured and my stomach became softer. "Thanks sweet friend," I said. "Friends like you, are precious and rare."

Not only did this interaction bring my girlfriend and I closer, it also helped heal my mother wound. As I stated earlier, growing up, my mother often said, "Don't cry." She learned that from having five brothers who said those words to her when she was a young girl. I was breaking a pattern that ran deep and my girlfriend was part of that healing.

If we don't learn to share our emotional parts in a healthy way with friends, family and partners who we trust, we rob our self of intimacy with them and the opportunity to create deeper, more satisfying connections. Unexpressed emotions, images and past memories can lie dormant in our bodies. When we slow down and bring presence to our body's sensations and gently dance around the edges of our physical pain, emotions often rise to the top.

When we learn to embrace all aspects of our self, we can start to listen to and honor our physical sensations and negative emotions. We can learn how to steer away from negative thoughts and how to observe negative emotions that come up without acting on them. As a result, we shift old, unconscious, negative belief patterns and emotions that are held in our bodies. When difficult emotions and sensations arise and are seen though the eyes of love, they can be understood with compassion. Eventually, they will pass through in a healthy way.

One morning while being present with my body, I observed some tightness in my jaw. I began massaging it. After several minutes my jaw began to relax. Then another painful sensation arose in my upper left back. I placed a rock between the mattress and my back near the tightness. The weight of my body on the rock allowed me to give focused attention to the area for several minutes. I softly took some deep breaths, breathing into the tightness. Sadness came up. As I softened and embraced the emotion, tears started to flow. Then a few images of Tim, my ex-partner from several years before, popped up. I continued to be present and more information came to me.

We were at his house having a conversation about our past relationships. Tim became upset about something I had said to one of his past lovers the summer before. I could see his face; his eyes were pierced with anger. The memory continued to play in my mind. Tim was furious and told me to get my things and leave. I stayed with the memory for a while.

**I had unknowingly held on to this memory
and it was stored in my body.**

I didn't understand why he was so angry. *What had I done?* Tim's anger was directed toward me and I obviously had allowed some of that pain into my heart. I kept comforting myself as I saw the image and felt the feelings of sadness and confusion. *I was willing to listen to his needs. Why was he taking this out on me?* I could see that my intentions were pure. I reassured myself, *I did nothing wrong.* After giving myself as much empathy as I needed, I began to have some for him too.

**I was amazed at how when I gave myself
enough empathy, empathy for others would
almost immediately followed.**

Tim didn't know any better. He didn't have the skills to identify his emotions in the moment and ask for what he needed. More thoughts of compassion and forgiveness popped in. *Tim was doing the best he could in the moment of his evolution. The anger was misdirected. It was nothing personal.* The back of my chest area began to soften.

Empowered realizations sprang up. *I have no interest in creating friendships with those who do not own their negative emotions and reactions. I am not interested in friends or people who project anger on to me and who don't take responsibility for their anger right away.* I felt emotionally safe and loved while giving myself this reassurance. A new priority and bar was set.

> **I made a commitment to having only intimate relationships with those who own their negative emotions and negative thoughts and who don't project them on to me.**

As we take time to be present with our bodies, sensations, thoughts and emotions, we reap the benefits of Self-love and Self-knowledge. It is then we become healthy, empowered individuals. As we develop the inner awareness skills to observe and express what is going on in our physical, emotional and mental bodies, we learn to break out of old, patterned conditioning from our childhood that no longer serves us. We give space and opportunities for old wounds to be healed. We then can move forward in creating a healthy relationship with our Self as well as with those we love and care about.

THOUGHTS, EMOTIONS, PHYSICAL SENSATIONS AND THEIR INTERCONNECTEDNESS - PRACTICES

Do one practice a day.
If you enjoy it, circle the practice and
add it to your wellness tool box.

DAY 1 PRACTICE
Daily Observation of Thoughts, Emotions and Physical Sensations

Make your inner health a priority. Do this by going inward every morning and repeatedly throughout your day. Use gentleness and kindness while you observe whatever thoughts, emotions and bodily sensations may be arising.

Find a comfortable spot to be still and go inward. Become present to your mind's thoughts, heart's emotions and body's sensations. Keep an inquisitive, non-judgmental attitude as you ask the following questions.

About Your Thoughts: *Am I focused on the mental activity in my head or am I present and in my body? _____ Is the thought in the present moment? _____ In the past? _____ In the future? _____ Is this thought important to do, right now? _____ Can I wait to do it later? _____ Am I having a lot of thoughts? _____ Just one or two thoughts? _____ Are my thoughts peaceful? _____ Creative? _____ Are my thoughts analytical? _____ Worrisome? _____ Are my thoughts judgmental? _____ Is this thought destructive? _____ Is this thought helpful? _____ Can I observe my thoughts without getting lost and attaching to them? _____*

About Your Emotions: Am I feeling sad? ____ Bored? ____ Fearful? ____ Anxious? ____ Frustrated? ____ Confused? ____ Or another contracting emotion? ____ Am I feeling relaxed? ____ Content? ____ Joyful? ____ Curious? ____ Happy? ____ Or another expansive emotion? ____ Am I blaming or making other people responsible for my emotions? ____ What keeps me from exploring and accepting my emotions? ____ What keeps me from expressing my emotions? ____

About Your Physical Sensations: Are there sensations in my body right now? ____ Is there tension? ____ Is it painful (intense)? ____ How would I describe the sensations? ____ Can I feel a part of my body that is relaxed and open? ____ Can I feel a part of my body that is contracted and tight? ____ Can I relax the tight parts in my body? ____

DAY 2 PRACTICE
Investigating Negative Emotions;
Locating Them in the Body

When you experience negative emotions, ask yourself, what emotion am I experiencing?

1. *Am I feeling, scared, fearful, nauseated, overwhelmed, sick, tired, sad, angry, irritated, frustrated, apprehensive, resistant, exhausted, drained and so on? Identify the emotion(s).*

   _____

   _____

2. *Am I able to locate where this negative emotion is in my body? If so, describe the area in your body, where you feel the emotion.*

   _____

   _____

3. *Keep your attention focused on your body and ask, "Does this emotion want to be expressed?" ____ If so, allow yourself to feel the emotion. Stay with your breath and soften as you allow the emotions to come up and move through. Perhaps there is some grief; feel the love and let the emotion move through. Perhaps there is some anger; engage in a growl and let it move through. If any fear of feeling the emotion rises, notice the fear or resistance in your body. If the emotion dissipates, observe that.*

4. *Check in with the area in your body where you located the negative emotion in your body. Connect to your breath and affirm, "It is safe to feel. It is safe to let go.". Visualize soothing, loving energy around the area in your body where you located the negative emotion. Relax into this healing energy and receive.*

5. *How do you feel? How does your body feel? Can you see how your body is connected to your emotions?*

_____

_____

When you feel complete with this practice, bring yourself back to the present moment, by taking a few deep breaths. Thank yourself for connecting to your heart and body.

DAY 3 PRACTICE
Interconnectedness of Physical Sensations, Emotions, Thoughts and Images

Begin by observing what is going on inside of your body. Locate a physical sensation or an area of pain that you would like to explore. Use your mind's eye, and observe the sensations in a relaxed manner. Be still and reflect while observing the sensa-

tion(s) and ask yourself the following questions?

1. *Can I move my attention into the center of this sensation or is the pain too great?*

If the sensation is too intense, see if you are able to bring your awareness farther away from the heart of the intensity and connect to the outer edges of the sensation. Place your attention as close to the center of the pain/sensation that you possibly can and then move your attention back out to the edges. Do the edges of the sensation(s) soften, move or shift in a subtle way or do they stay the same? Does the intensity increase, decrease or stay the same?

---

2. *Is it possible to let the intensity of the sensation be the way it is without trying to force it to change, go away or heal? (That can be a healing itself!)*

---

3. *Is there a feeling or emotion arising along with the sensation or behind the sensation? If so, can you name the emotion?*

---

4. *Can I nurture the area and emotion by giving it presence, a soft breath and/or placing a hand or finger on it?*

---

5. *Are any thoughts or images arising? If so, what are they? Do they remind you of someone, a situation or a story in the past? (If not, that's fine.)*

6. *If an image from the past arises, remind yourself that the image is from the past and has nothing to do with this moment. Notice if any emotion rises from the past situation, but do not attach to it. Allow the emotion to move through your body.*

7. *Ask yourself, how would I have taken care of myself or done things differently in the past if I were able? How will I take care of myself now?*

8. *Visualize yourself in the past situation with more power, skill and centeredness. What would you say or do to take care of yourself and/or speak your truth, if you knew what you know now?*

When you feel complete, watch the images and stories pass by like clouds in the sky. Now imagine yourself wrapped in a warm blanket of love. Appreciate yourself and all the new growth and tools you have. Remind yourself of the moment you are in, take a few deep breaths and remember the loving presence that is surrounding your heart, mind and body. Bask in this love and peace until you are ready to move forward with your day.

Chapter 5

LOVING, LIFE FORCE ENERGY: QI, KI, PRANA

"All energy comes from a higher source.
All energy is the higher source.
We don't create it. We just tap into it.
Call it what you will.
It is the essence of life's creative force which is,
in and of itself, miraculous."

STEPHEN LEWIS

I BEGAN EVERY MORNING REMINDING MYSELF THAT HEALING energy is always running through me. Even though I was experiencing discomfort and pain in my teeth, neck and jaw, I focused on the space and light around the pain. Just knowing that this spacious energy was around my body and around the pain, soothed my fears and relaxed my nervous system. Even though the tight spots seemed solid under my fingers, I knew better. *This healing, loving energy runs through everything.*

I had been interested in energy, quantum mechanics and physics for a long time. By no means do I clam to be a scientist, but I do know that science has proven that each atom and molecule do not even physically touch. There is space between and around every atom, down to the very smallest particle. Everything in this universe has space around it. Therefore, the same spaciousness and order that is in the universe, is also in my body. I would remind myself; *the blocks of pain and tight tissue I experience are not solid. They are constantly in motion and are rearranging themselves, just as the universe is constantly shifting and rearranging.*

I reflected on this even more. The spaciousness is around every thought too. There is energy in between the words, consonants and vowels. I listened to that space between the thoughts and noticed it was completely silent. I observed the space between the thoughts and words and saw that there was only space around it all. As well, the majority of my thoughts had nothing to do with this very present moment.

The more I put my attention on the space instead of the words in my head, my thoughts slowed down and eventually dissolved into the background. The spacious, healing energy came to the forefront. I became more and more relaxed as I rested in this loving, spacious energy. Soon, the tension was gone. It was a softening process. As I surrendered, tears tenderly fell from my eyes.

Receiving so much loving energy had not always been easy for me. Many, many, years ago, I discovered this life force energy in my body.

I remembered after a breakup with a boyfriend, I was lying in bed with such heaviness on my chest. The relationship didn't end in a loving way and I was integrating all that had occurred. I put my hands on my chest to soothe my heart. I felt loving energy where my hands were. I was fascinated with the sensations in my body. The presence I gave through my hands comforted my heart and a tingling flow of energy soon spread throughout my entire body. I didn't have words for it.

Initially, I didn't want to label this energy or put it in a box, as it was beyond words and boundaries.

Later on, a friend gave me a name for this energy. She called it "Reiki;" which is a Japanese word; "rei" meaning light, "ki" meaning life force energy. I found that having words for the experience helped me connect to others who had similar experiences.

My friend told me Reiki classes were available, so I took one. In the Reiki I class, the facilitator explained that Reiki means universal life force energy and that everything has this life force energy around and through it. The class also taught us that we each have our own unique soul's life force energy and that the universal life force energy is like the ocean and the individual soul's energy is like a drop of water in that ocean. I had already been tapping into and experiencing the all-encompassing universal life force energy and became even more curious about this energy.

**Scientifically this made sense. $E=mc^2$.
Einstein's equation, was something I had read
about and knew was one of the foundations
for Western Society's understanding of energy.**

Basically, the equation points to the relationship of energy and mass. This lead me to understand that all form is matter and all matter is energy and all energy is space and light. Every thing is composed of one invisible fabric. Eastern cultures have known of this primal energy force for thousands of years, but in our Western culture, it is a fairly new concept.

There are many names for universal life force energy – Energy, Reiki, Chi, Qi, light, prana, mana, source energy, healing energy, unconditional love, and more. There are many healing modalities that consciously utilize the healing effects of life force energy. Reiki, Tai-Chi, Chi-Gong, Aikido, acupuncture, massage, sound healing, yoga, breath and mindfulness meditation practices are just some of them.

> **In a very simple way, I like to think of energy**
> **as the glue that is holding us all together.**
> **Another name for the glue is love.**

Love holds us all together! Energy has no definite shape; it is always shifting and changing. Energy doesn't judge or criticize; it is neutral. The entire universe is made up of this loving energy. Everything and everyone can be seen and experienced as a continuum of energetic vibration to some degree or another. And we all have the ability to positively charge to this loving energy.

Even though my teeth, neck and other areas of my body ached and felt uncomfortable, I continued to practice focusing on the spacious, healing energy around the pain. I would lay in bed, sometimes for hours, relaxing my nervous system and calming my soul as I surrendered deeply to this energy. It was always there, expansive and relaxing. As I focused on the space and surrendered, the energy would move into various areas of my body, causing tingling sensations and sometimes, heat would arise.

> **What I loved about this energy was that it had**
> **a mind of its own. It knew exactly where to**
> **go in my body. It was beyond my analytical**
> **mind and fearful thoughts.**

When the chattering thoughts would slow down and settle, my sensitivity to the energy would increase. Sometimes, I would focus on light, like the sun, as if I was receiving rays of light in every cell of my body. This focusing seemed to amplify the energy. I began working with this energy in a very deep way in my body.

It was simple; wherever I placed my hands on my body, the energy would follow. I would lay my hands on my jaw and the energy would follow. When the area had had enough, I could sense it. That part of my body became relaxed and open and there was a feeling of being content and complete. Next, I moved my hands next to my head, and then my neck. The tension would open, eventually diminish or even go away.

After receiving enough of the healing, loving energy, chattering thoughts ceased and an inner guidance would arise and direct my next step.

It became clear to me when to get up and do things like make a phone call, schedule an appointment or stretch slowly while integrating this energy into my next move. This loving energy is what kept me moving with inner ease through this difficult situation with the pain.

One morning, after a deep session of surrendering and receiving healing energy in my body, I became aware that I needed to communicate with my endodontist, Dr. Geminiz that I was still having pain in the molar where he had performed a root canal a few weeks earlier. Another one of my molars was also having issues. I picked up the phone and made an appointment to see him the following week.

The day came and before leaving for the appointment, I sat in my car in my driveway, comforting my nerves. The beautiful thing about this energy is I could tap into it anyplace and anytime. I put my feet up on the driving dash, laid my head back and chose a favorite rock from the collection I had on the floor in my car. I had gathered them over the years from various places and they became very useful healing tools. I used different rocks to do my own version of an acupuncture treatment and pressure point therapy.

As I placed a sharper rock under my occipital ridge, my thoughts quickly settled. I could feel the energy in my body. As I surrendered to it, my jaw became relaxed. Within 15 minutes, I was re-charged and ready to drive to the appointment. I was in a state of bliss as I drove to my appointment with Dr. Geminiz. *Wow, I'm driving in the Bliss Zone*, I thought to myself.

When I arrived at Dr. Geminiz' office, I had a few minutes to spare. My first inclination was to get up and go in. *Wait. Why would I want to go into his office, when I could sit and receive more loving energy?* I put my feet up on the dashboard again and received. I was learning Self-love at a level I hadn't allowed myself to experience before. The pain was an impetus for this deeper Self-love. The more I surrendered to the energy, the more I yearned to receive and experience more of its love.

I entered Dr. Geminiz' office. His assistant directed me to one of his treatment rooms, then she left. I wiggled my way into the office chair and looked around at the surroundings. I liked the way Dr. Geminiz had set up his room. There was a large window with a view of a garden sanctuary outside. Bright flowers and green bushes by a water fountain caught my eye. *Nature is so expansive and filled with light.* It reminded me of the loving energy that expands through everything. I could feel the energy pulsating in my hands.

His assistant came in and took x-rays of the root canal and the other molar where I was experiencing pain. After she processed the x-rays, she put them up on the screen. She must have noticed the strong energy that was moving through me as she put her hand up toward mine and asked, "Do you feel anything?"

"I sure do. Energy." She and I had talked before and she felt comfortable around me. She began curiously moving her hands around mine.

"I've taken quite a few Reiki classes and I've been running a lot of energy lately," I said, as I placed my hand directly in front of hers.

"I can feel it," she said. "I'm pretty sensitive and I've explored some of this as well."

Our conversation lasted until the doctor came in.

"Hi Gerilyn," Dr. Geminiz said with a bright tone of voice.

"Hi Dr. Geminiz," my voice lowered. I didn't want to sound too happy as I needed to show him I had pain and something needed to be done about it. "The root canal that you did a few weeks ago still hurts. The other molar on the bottom right side is also painful.

I don't think these root canals are working," I said with a tired, exhausted expression.

He pointed to the x-rays. "Well, they do work for the majority of individuals, but there is a small percentage of individuals they don't work for." He paused. "There is nothing problematic showing up on these x-rays, but I don't want you to be in pain." He looked at me with kind, compassionate eyes. "X-rays don't always pick up the tiniest fractures. The only other solution would be to have the tooth that had the root canal extracted. I think we should wait with the other bottom molar and keep an eye on it."

I nodded in agreement and hid my inner excitement. *Yes, no more pain in that molar.* "Thank you Dr. Geminiz," I replied in a monitored, slow and tired tone.

"I'll get you a referral. Sit here for a moment while I try to get you in as soon as possible."

He went up to the front desk, made a few phone calls and came right back. I felt heard, cared for and loved. "Dr. Gregory is booked. I know another oral surgeon..." Dr. Geminiz recommended Dr. Chee and told me he himself had had a tooth pulled by Dr. Chee. I felt reassured and scheduled an appointment for the following week to have yet another molar pulled. The upcoming extraction sounds like a weird thing to be grateful for, but I was. I drove home with joy, in hopes that the pain in that tooth would be gone very soon.

As soon as I got home, I laid on my bed, focused on my breath and observed the sensations in my body. I placed my hands on each side of my jaw and the thoughts settled. The energy was subtle at first and became stronger as I sighed, making effortless sounds. "Ahhhhh" and "Mmmm." I could feel the buzz of energy in my body.

Within several minutes, there was a current of energy running through my hands, between my temples, and into my neck and shoulders. The energy stream intensified and a flood gate of pulsating vibrations ran through me.

I stayed in a surrendered state for a long, long time, adjusting my hands and fingers to various places of tension in my body. And then something that didn't happened very often occurred. My body realigned itself on its own. First, I felt a little energy moving in my spine. Then my back opened as I felt a few crackles. The vertebrae in my neck and back popped a little more. My jaw realigned itself too. The energy was guiding this whole process. Sensations of heat and yawning accompanied the release.

I was amazed. *How could this be?* Even though I was so exhausted from the day, lying on my bed, doing nothing, I felt so alive. I could see how this energy was the most vital part of my existence. As I lay there, I contemplated the movement and spaciousness of this loving energy. With every interaction, anytime I lay a hand on someone or myself, every time I hug, I am giving and receiving this loving energy. Healing energy is attempting to flow through my hands, my feet, my eyes, my mouth and every cell of my body, every minute of the day.

I was surrendering and receiving more energy than ever. Old, stuck energies were being addressed and I was shifting energetically, physically, emotionally and mentally. Of course, the surgeries were shifting my teeth and jaw situation too. The old negative beliefs and fears about doctors not caring about my needs were transforming into compassion. I was also receiving more love and Self-love and becoming stronger at listening to my inner guidance and speaking my truth.

I was shifting deeply. I began viewing my situation as a long, long detoxification process.

Energetic detoxification can show up in many forms: yawning, burping, tension, intense pain, sickness, simple common colds, a runny nose, headaches, diarrhea, fatigue, nausea

and many other forms of release. When we detox, we are simply cleansing our bodies, minds and emotions. This can be done at a physical level through cleanses and fasting. It can also happen energetically through receiving expansive, loving energy.

Our bodies speak to us when something isn't right. It tells us when something needs to be released and cleansed. Our bodies are connected to our emotions, and emotions are connected to our thoughts, and our emotions and thoughts are connected to our bodies. We can use our bodies as a gauge to discover what needs to be released and healed. As we learn to receive loving energy, painful past conditioning can rise and be released. When we e-mote (energy in motion) with a good cry or release anger in an appropriate way, we free ourselves. As we learn to let go of fearful, mental condition-ing, the traumatized parts of our brain begin to heal and produce loving thought patterns. As we release at a cellular level, our bodies shift and our hearts open to more and more of this loving energy. Being gentle with ourselves is necessary as old patterns pass and new ways of thinking and living gradually emerge.

Unfortunately, the traditional health care system rarely acknowledges or addresses energetic detoxification processes that go on in our bodies, emotions and minds. Western medicine practitioners often see the symptoms of the body as the problem and prescribe medication before addressing the whole person. Medications are sometimes needed, but medications can also end up suppressing deeper issues that need to be resolved. Tragically, most traditional doctors are unaware of the detoxification process. Unless doctors are trained in energy healing and other holistic modalities, medication sadly remains the main solution to many health issues.

My personal detoxification process was multifaceted and very challenging on all levels. I couldn't eat hard foods and had to rely on juicing to get my nutrition. I said "goodbye" to pizza, candy bars and other hard to eat foods that had no nutrition. Instead, I added a glass of juice which included chard, carrot, beet, lettuce, cucumber, celery and ginger, to my meals everyday. I added the leftover pulp to soups, refried beans and other soft, mashed dishes.

It was an energetic adjustment on all levels, physically, emotionally and mentally. I often felt exhausted and excess weight melted away. My mind became clearer than ever. I didn't take supplements or medication for the exhaustion because I understood that being tired was part of the detoxification process and nurtured myself through the process.

The beauty of connecting to our unique soul's life force energy and the universal life force energy is that it is always there, whether we are aware of it or not. There is nothing anyone can ever do to separate from this life force energy. As we learn to stop and sense our bodies and the space in which the body resides, we can begin to experience this healing energy and use it to recharge and heal our systems in the healthiest ways.

LOVING, LIFE FORCE ENERGY - PRACTICES

Do one practice a day.
If you enjoy it, circle the practice and
add it to your wellness tool box.

DAY 1 PRACTICE
Sensing and Using Healing Energy in
Your Hands and for Your Body

Energy is in, through and all around us. We can tap into this healing life force energy at any time and it can nourish us physically, emotionally and mentally. This healing energy can restore our muscles, organs and cells, as well as relax our minds and calm our nervous system.

1. *Bring your hands together as close as you can without touching. What do you sense between your hands?*

   ....

   ....

   Energy sensations are very subtle. You may (or may not) feel heat or an energetic pull between your hands. Experiment, knowing there's no right or wrong way to explore.

2. *Slowly bring your hands farther apart. What do you sense now?*

   ....

   ....

3. *Put your hands a few inches apart and imagine that you*

are holding a small ball of invisible energy. Bring your hands farther apart as if you are holding a larger ball of energy. Move your hands in and out, playing with this ball of energy. Can you feel any sensations? How would you describe them?

....

....

4. *Now place your hands behind your head and focus on your breath. Bring your attention to the back of your head. Have the intention of bringing loving energy to your head through your hands. What sensations do you notice from your hands onto your head? (Keep your hands behind your head for as long as feels good.)*

....

....

5. *When you feel you have received enough energy, move your hands to your heart. Slow your breath down and receive this healing energy for as long as feels good in the heart area.*

6. *Use your breath to help you focus inward, as you continue laying your hands on other parts of your body to receive loving energy: your shoulders, rib cage, stomach, alongside your thighs and hips, knees and wherever else on your body feels right for you. Make sure to pause between each hand placement and focus on your breath and the sensations in your hands.*

7. *After you feel complete, answer these questions.*

   a. How does your body feel?

....

....

b. *Can you feel the energy getting stronger in your hands and body? Describe the sensations in your hands and body.*

_____

_____

c. *Has your mind settled or relaxed? Describe your mind's activity.*

_____

_____

If you make this a daily practice, you will strengthen your connection to healing energy and become more sensitive and aware of its presence in your hands and body.

DAY 2 PRACTICE
Daily Energetic Body Scan

In this practice, you will scan your body from top to bottom from the place of awareness. Scanning is simply observing the body without wanting the experience to be different than it is. Scanning is similar to a mindful meditation in that the presence you give yourself will bring your attention into the present moment and allow you to connect to healing energy in your body. Below is a list of adjectives to use to describe the energetic sensations you may feel in your body.

Take a few deep breaths and settle into your body. Now bring your attention to the top of your head and ask these questions:

1. *Do you sense or experience heat? _____ Coolness? _____ Numbness? _____ Tingling? _____ Heaviness? _____ Lightness? _____ Tightness? _____ Openness? _____ Contractions? _____*

Expansiveness? ____ Is there a pulsating sensation? ____ Is there a stabbing sensation? ____

2. *Bring your attention into other parts of your body and use the same adjectives above to describe what you are sensing and noticing.*

   a. *What do you sense energetically around your forehead and eyes? Look at the adjectives above and write down the ones that are true for you.*

   _____

   _____

   b. *What do you notice around your jaw? (Look at the adjectives above.)*

   _____

   _____

   c. *Around the base of your neck?*

   _____

   _____

   d. *On the top of your shoulders?*

   _____

   _____

   e. *Down your arms? Your hands?*

   _____

   _____

   f. *Continue to bring your attention to other parts of your body using the same energetic descriptions above. Around and in your heart? ____ Solar plexus? ____ Upper back? ____ Belly? ____ Lower back? ____ Hips?*

_____ *Base of your spine? _____ Legs? _____ Knees? _____ Ankles? _____Feet? _____Any other part of the body you would like to include in your body scan? _____*

3. *Where in your body does it feel the most contracted and tight?*

_____

_____

4. *Where does it feel the most expansive and relaxed in your body?*

_____

_____

5. *Where in your body do you feel the coolest sensations?*

_____

_____

6. *Where do you feel the most heat?*

_____

_____

7. *Where are the most tingling sensations in your body?*

_____

_____

8. *Now connect to your breath and do a general scan of your entire body from top to bottom. Notice the different sensations and the energy that is around and runs through your body. How do you feel?*

_____

_____

Do this practice daily and you will become very aware of your body's energy field. Empty your mind and receive healing energy every day that will benefit your mind, body and emotions.

You might try doing this practice with a good friend, taking turns asking the questions above with each other. After facilitating the body scan, if it feels right, place your hands gently on the areas mentioned above, as guided of course. You may also want to put on some relaxing music to help relax the mind chatter.

DAY 3 PRACTICE
Visualization for Grounding and Centering

At the end of the day or week, our minds and bodies can feel disconnected and rather chaotic. On a daily basis, we have a myriad of experiences that can take us out of our own center. Because of this, we can sometimes feel scattered and/or spacey.

Grounding and re-centering after experiencing daily life events is extremely important. Grounding energetically helps us clear our minds of past events, release others' energies and come back into our bodies. In this way, we come back to the present moment and reconnect to a state of inner peace. Then we can integrate life's experiences, center into our hearts and get clarity.

Begin in a comfortable position with eyes open or closed. Think of a tree and how its roots go into the ground. Energetically, feel your feet and your body rooted in the earth. Visualize invisible energetic roots connecting you to the earth's core. With each breath, let go of any attachments to others or situations in the past and allow the mind to settle. As you release and relax, imagine yourself receiving the gift of the earth's healing energy.

See the earth's energy coming through your feet and twisting its way up your legs, into your hips and around the bottom of your spine and then through your stomach, heart, shoulders, arms, hands, neck, forehead and to the top of your head.

Take a few breaths and then visualize the sun's light rays moving from the top of your head twisting back down around the eyes, ears, neck, through your heart, arms, hands, upper back, lower back, hips, legs and feet. Imagine the light grounding you with your feet planted into the earth. Imagine yourself, like a tree grounded and calm.

Now, be silent for a while. Allow your body and mind to regenerate and receive as much loving energy as it needs.

As you come out of the visualization, take a few mindful breaths. You might also do a little movement. Perhaps swaying back and forth on your sitz bones or on your feet as you receive this loving energy.

See if you can stay connected to your internal self, earth's energy and the sensations you feel in your body while letting your surroundings in.

Know that you can repeat this process any time during your day.

Chapter 6

MEDITATION AND MINDFULNESS

*"When you lose touch with inner stillness,
you lose touch with your Self. When you lose touch
with your Self, you lose yourself in the world."*

Eckhart Tolle

The added stresses of having so many doctor's opinions and so many appointments, sometimes three a week, was overwhelming. Meeting friends, other community activities and even work had to take a back seat in order to deal with the pain in my teeth and so many doctors' visits. I needed alone time so I could be present with myself , my mind and my body, so that I could calm my nervous system and make important teeth and doctor decisions.

**I needed silence. I needed to witness the pain so
I could listen for what it was trying to tell me.**

That way I could hear the guidance of my inner truth instead of just following the doctor's orders. I used meditation to begin every day to calm my nerves, get clarity and take the next step. From this place of stillness, I could handle the chaos of my situation and center while filtering out the opinions and unnecessary input from so many doctors. My plans and appointments would often change. When they did, I was able to adjust with ease. Meditation was my inner respite.

The amount of stimulation and daily input most of us are exposed to can be overwhelming. People's thoughts and opinions, along with computers, radios, signs, billboards, e-mails and texts are constantly calling for our attention. The noise of the world can drown out our peaceful centeredness and intuitive sensing. Our lives are often overly structured with scheduled commitments. Our minds have little opportunity for free-flowing thinking and for experiencing freedom without obligations. Our minds have very little time to relax and we are seldom completely present in our bodies without any distractions. We often lose ourselves to the chaotic constraints of the world and don't even know it. (Cowan, 2014)

When we are mindful, we are aware of what is going on in and around us without judgment. Mindfulness is the practice of paying attention here and now with kindness and curiosity and then choosing your behavior (Mindful Schools, 2001). When we are aware of our breath, sounds in the room or the sensations in our body, we become conscious of the present moment. Mindfulness is a tool used in meditation. With meditation, we go within and observe our minds' thoughts, bodies' sensations and emotions. Meditation is used to achieve mentally and emotionally a calm state. There are many ways to be mindful and meditate. (Kabat-Zinn, 2019)

Through meditation, I learned to be an observer, witnessing my thoughts, emotions, and sensations from an energetic distance.

This energetic distance was important because it created space between me and that which I was observing. The ability to observe my thoughts, images, emotions, and physical sensations at a distance allowed me to witness rather than attach to these things. Meditation helped me move through situations that were physically painful and mentally exhausting with the doctors and their many opinions.

**Meditation helped me get clarity from
within and let go of all the confusion,
fear and excess thinking.**

The viewpoint of the observer is witnessing without judgment. There is space between the observer and what is being observed. The observer is neutral and does not insist on or want anything to be different than it is. The thoughts, emotions, sensations and images are held with gentleness, spaciousness and neutrality. (Sovik, 2014)

Observing is simple, but not easy. We often get caught up in thoughts and stories and forget we are there merely to witness them. When we attach to thoughts, emotions, images and sensations, we often believe the stories our minds are telling us. We then complain and argue about reality because we want something to be different than it is and in doing so, we often end up judging ourselves and others. We hold on to thoughts tightly, the good, the bad, the beautiful and the ugly ones. We then base our identity and others identities on those made-up stories. When we attach and believe the stories of our minds, we create inner suffering.

From the viewpoint of the observer, thoughts come and go. They are not the truth. There is no grasping or wanting from life. Life is not personal. There is no suffering because there is no attachment or believing the monkey-mind chatter of the mind and all of its stories, fears and judgments. Sensations arise, emotions arise, thoughts arise and move through us. There is no desire to get rid of the thoughts, emotions, sensations and images. In fact, if we find ourselves pushing thoughts away, we end up fighting with them. This resistance creates more tension and discomfort. In meditation, everything is welcomed, accepted and observed from a distance.

When we apply meditation and mindful practices to life, we don't make one experience better than another. Personal preferences disappear. We are in the moment and experiencing whatever is from a centered, neutral place. We react less to emotional ups and downs and become able to ride the roller coaster of life with our hands in the air, centered in our bodies, instead of hanging on for dear life.

After arguing with reality and making the experience with my teeth wrong, I felt depressed. *This shouldn't be happening. Why me?* The pity party got old after a while.

When I witnessed the thoughts and pain from the viewpoint of the observer, I could see that I was not this situation. I was not the pain. What was happening to me was merely another situation that my soul was experiencing. The depression was gone. I could see that my thoughts were mostly about the past and the future and not about anything actually happening in the present moment.

Only when I was able to observe in this non-attached way, did I feel and experience a deeper soul love.

When the monkey-mind quiets or we learn to simply ignore its chattering, when we are present with our hearts, we feel rested and loved. Our heart rates lower, our pulse comes back into balance, our breath slows down and our bodies relax.

Meditation helps put our emotional, physical and mental bodies back in balance. It's so easy to take on stress; fear-based thoughts creep in and before we know it, our peace is gone. We have allowed our monkey-minds to take over. We walk around in a hurried pace, in our heads and disconnected from our bodies. Through meditation, we acknowledge the busy, analytical (monkey) mind and although we see the thoughts, we do not make them a priority. We remember the space between our Self and the thoughts. Then we can drop in and once again feel calm and centered.

It was time to get another molar pulled. This was the second one. I was on my way to Dr. Chee's office. I had already met with him a couple of weeks prior for a consultation and x-rays. When I reached his office, I had several extra minutes before the procedure. I meditated a little more receiving the loving energy, staying present with my body. The more present I was in my body, the more present I became with my surroundings.

I took a slow, mindful walk, connecting to my body and breath; enjoying the plants and trees that were part of the office landscape. *Ahhh*, the simple things gave me such pleasure!

I walked into Dr. Chee's office and was greeted by the receptionist. Then his assistant came and ushered me into a room with a surgical chair. I sat down and she adjusted the chair so I could lay back and relax my head and jaw. As she began to rearrange and prepare the room for surgery, I turned my focus to my breath to meditate. In the middle of her preparation she asked, "How are you doing?"

"Oh, I'm on a meditation vacation," I spoke, with a relaxed, smirk on my face. The assistant grinned back and played along. "For how long?"

«Oh, just for right now, as I sit back in this comfy, relaxing surgical chair." We laughed a bit and I explained my process of meditation to her and how it relaxes my mind and my body. I told her how much meditation helped during a previous tooth extraction and how in general, these practices have helped me through other invasive and aggressive procedures with my teeth. She was intrigued and impressed.

When the surgeon walked in, the assistant shared with him about my meditation practice and how it helps me to relax during surgeries. "How many of your patients smile while getting ready for surgery?" I asked the surgeon while grinning.

"Not many," he replied. "Maybe 2% of my patients." The tooth came out easily and I was successful staying calm and centered through it all.

There are as many ways to meditate and be mindful as there are people that walk the earth. Meditation and mindfulness practices can be experienced sitting, standing, laying down and in practically any position. Practices can also be done while eating, gardening, walking, dancing, biking, running and cleaning, in any place or with any activity you can you imagine. Meditation and mindfulness practices are for all ages. Being mindful is simply being in the present moment, observing what is without judgment.

Sometimes the beginning stages of meditation can seem frivolous, even useless. Often the mind chatter just won't stop and the body sensations are uncomfortable. This is typical and to be expected. The more we practice, the easier it gets. The breath can be used as an anchoring point and can assist in breathing through these uncomfortable edges. Being mindful of the breath helps us stay in the present moment. We are so used to focusing on our thoughts and emotions that sometimes, it takes a while for them to settle down. By using the breath as the anchor, we distract our self from our thoughts (Simon, 1999).

The more we practice meditation and mindfulness, eventually the treasures of Self-love and Self-awareness open and we can receive many empowering and healing benefits. As we observe and stay curious about the brain's activity, we can discover the difference between the monkey-mind (repetitive, analytical, judgmental, negative, controlling thoughts) and thoughts that are useful, true and helpful in our lives. Through meditation and mindful practices, we can get-to-know our brains, thoughts, emotions, body sensations through loving presence so that we can make better choices and live more satisfying lives.

I began to ask myself.
Who is it that is witnessing?
Who is the observer?

I knew I wasn't the many fearful thoughts that passed through. I could see that the pain would come and go. And even the emotions that I observed would come and go. It was an inquiry that kept me interested and fascinated with myself, my thoughts, emotions and intense sensations.

Beyond our sensations, beyond our emotions, beyond our thoughts, lies the observer. Some call this observer Higher Mind, Higher Self, Self, Awareness, Higher Consciousness, the Knower, Soul Self, or Spiritual Self. Regardless of what we call the observer, it is that which unconditionally accepts all our experiences without judgment. The observer watches and witnesses without wanting or needing, without suppressing or trying to fix or change anything. Remembering the observer through meditation can lead to a wide variety of benefits such as effortless decision making, emotional regulation, better memory processing, expanded freedom and inner happiness, all of which are not dependent on the world or outer circumstances (Oz, 2020).

MEDITATION AND MINDFULNESS - PRACTICES

Do one practice a day.
If you enjoy it, circle the practice and
add it to your wellness tool box.

DAY 1 PRACTICE
Beginning Meditation Practice

In meditation, thoughts, emotions and physical sensations are observed from a place of non-judgment and non-attachment. There is an experience of "space" between you and the thoughts, emotions and sensations that you are observing. This place of witnessing is sometimes called awareness or your Higher Self.

Begin by finding a place where there are little to no distractions, perhaps in a quiet room at home, in nature, in your car or on a park bench.

Close your eyes and settle into your body. Notice that you are aware of everything that is happening in this moment. From this place of being aware, begin to observe the breath. Without trying to change or alter it in any way, notice the breath coming in and flowing out as you inhale and exhale. Notice that the breath is happening all by itself, as if the body is being breathed. Use the breath to anchor your attention and keep coming back to it so you don't get lost in your thoughts. Surround the thoughts with loving energy without attaching to them. Watch the thoughts drift by like clouds in the sky. Notice, when you are present, you are more like the ever-present sky than like the clouds drifting within it. If you find yourself getting lost in the thoughts, gently center again by focusing on your breath. Don't be hard or too strict with yourself, just explore and observe your breath and thoughts as gently as possible.

Practice meditation every day; but don't ever get too rigid. Begin with one minute, then five minutes, then twenty minutes and work your way up at a pace that works for you. There are no rules. Stay fascinated and curious. You may want to set your timer so you aren't thinking about how much time goes by.

There are various stages in meditation one goes through. In the beginning stages, it can seem difficult because there are just so many thoughts occurring and meditating feels useless. But be assured, it is not. If you do find yourself "fighting" with your thoughts, wanting the thoughts to leave or be gone, more discomfort and agony will follow. But that too is a learning process.

Just notice your resistance to your thoughts. Again, this can be an uncomfortable stage as one learns how to work with this rhythm. Eventually, you'll discover fighting with thoughts is useless and you'll catch yourself and stop all efforts to do so. Instead of fighting with the thoughts, you may try getting up and moving and coming back to meditating later. Eventually the thoughts will settle on their own. If you feel inclined to, try adding some of the other tools in this book to help you get over this uncomfortable hump, such as touch (like using acupressure), tuning into nature and listening to soothing music (without words). These tools can help you focus on something other than your thoughts.

As your inner exploration and curiosity strengthens, as well as moments of deep relaxation and peace, you'll want to hang out longer in meditation. With enough time and practice, a true and deep desire for this introspective respite will develop. Remember that every meditation experience is different and it is essential to be gentle along the way.

DAY 2 PRACTICE
Open Space Meditation

Begin by getting into a comfortable position and relaxing into your body.

1. *Can you imagine empty space or loving presence around your thoughts as they rise? _____ Can you notice or imagine space in between or around the words? _____ Can you experience the silent background in which thoughts occur? _____*

2. *Now bring awareness to your body. Can you imagine space or loving presence around your body? _____ Space between your ears? _____ Loving energy between your fingers? _____ Between your toes? _____*

3. *Find a specific area of tension or pain in the body. Can you imagine spaciousness around the pain or tension?_____*

Continue this practice with fascination and curiosity for as long as you like. (Check out Open Focus Meditation in Health and Well-Being Support Groups at the end of the book for more meditations of this kind.)

DAY 3 PRACTICE
Distinguishing Between Your Higher
Mind and Your Monkey-Mind

After you've been meditating for a while, you will begin to notice the difference between the chattering of the mind (monkey-mind) and your intuitive, Higher Mind (Awareness/Higher Self). When observing the monkey-mind, always make sure you are being gentle. Do not make any thoughts right or wrong; that's just more monkey-mind! This practice is not about get rid of the monkey-mind, but differentiating between it and the intuitive, Higher Mind. When you are able to make this distinction, you will feel more empowered to choose the thoughts that serve you rather than to be run by thoughts that don't.

Relax into a meditative state as you observe your thoughts. If you have a limited amount of time, you may want to set a timer for

5-10 minutes. Then ask yourself the following questions about the thoughts that are rising.

1. *Is this thought in the past or future? ____ monkey-mind (But not always. Looking at the past can also be an opportunity for inner reflection.)*

2. *Is this thought about acceptance, forgiveness and healing a situation? ____ Higher Mind*

3. *Is this thought giving you clarity? ____ Higher Mind*

4. *Does this thought produce anger, fear, sadness or anxiety in the body? ____ monkey-mind (Also an opportunity for exploration of possible suppressed emotions that could be addressed for deeper healing. See Chapter 10: Emotional Intelligence)*

5. *Are the thoughts trying to find answers and do you find yourself in a mental loop? ____ monkey-mind*

6. *Are the thoughts incessantly repeating themselves with worry and concern? ____ monkey-mind*

7. *Is the thought simple, comforting and pure? ____ Higher Mind*

8. *Does this thought bring about joy, inner peace and tranquility? ____ Higher Mind*

9. *Is the thought about the desire for justification? ____ monkey-mind*

10. *Are these thoughts giving you a breakthrough or another perspective in life that is useful? ____ Higher Mind*

11. *Does the thought have a "should" in it or does the thought want something to be different than it is? ____ monkey-mind*

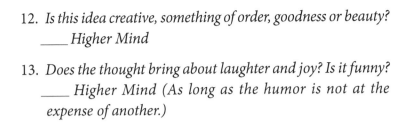

12. *Is this idea creative, something of order, goodness or beauty?*
    ____ *Higher Mind*

13. *Does the thought bring about laughter and joy? Is it funny?*
    ____ *Higher Mind (As long as the humor is not at the expense of another.)*

Through consistent observation, you will find subtler and more finely-tuned ways to discern the monkey-mind and the Higher Mind. After seeing the difference between the monkey-mind and Higher Mind, you may find yourself ignoring and dismissing the monkey-mind thoughts and remembering what is actually true. You may start to automatically visualize spacious, loving energy around all the chatter.

We all have monkey-mind thoughts and having tools to deal with them is important for our mental health and emotional well-being. The shift toward making our Higher Minds and our hearts the primary focus takes time. With perseverance, gentleness and patience, however, you will to experience more clarity, insight, truth, laughter, play, confidence, peace and relaxation in the mind and body.

Chapter 7

INNER INQUIRY QUESTIONS

"The intuitive mind is a sacred gift, and the rational mind is a faithful servant. We have created a society that honors the servant and has forgotten the gift."

ALBERT EINSTEIN

MANY OF MY QUESTIONS REMAINED UNANSWERED. TWO TEETH had been pulled and the implant that had failed was pulled with no new implant in its place. I was grateful that I was moving forward with less pain than before, but still had to deal with the pain in the other molars that would come and go and seemed to be getting more intense. I wondered, *perhaps I notice the residual pain in the other molars now because the pain of the failed implant is gone.*

My dentist suggested I take another round of penicillin just incase there was an infection and that was causing the pain. *Taking more antibiotics didn't seem like the solution.* He went back to his original recommendation of orthognathic jaw surgery. *No thank you, not if I can help it.* My endodontist thought I may need to re-do a couple old root canals. *That didn't seem quite right either.* One of my oral surgeons thought the lingering pain in my molars was just referred pain from another tooth. *Not sure about that.* I had a lot of fear, anxiety and unanswered questions. I didn't want to follow doctor's orders blindly. I didn't want to waste my money and time, and was tired of listening to all the differing opinions and suggestions. I began a daily process of self-investigation to find truth.

My inner inquiry process had various dimensions. First, I would focus on a problem and ask a "yes" or "no" question around that issue. This would help simplify the process so I could better sense my inner voice and intuitive body. Sometimes, when my stories and fearful thoughts got in the way of seeing something clearly, I would question my perceptions. Then eventually, I would continue to more open-ended self-inquiry questions.

**Self-investigation and inquiry would help
me know and see what is really true.**

When I asked the deeper questions in a space of detachment and unconditional love, the best direction would always reveal itself. I listened carefully and dove into deep waters. I was open to all possibilities. As I sat back and let my psyche settle, I would watch and wait for my inner wisdom to express itself. The revelations would come from a place in my body, an intuitive knowing, not from my analytical mind. Only the deepest parts of myself, my intuitive, Higher Mind, would know these inner truths.

**Distinguishing between my heart's wisdom
and my mind's conditioned logic took time,
a quiet space and stillness.**

Upon asking a question, I noticed the busy, chattering mind typically answers first and with more words than are necessary. This is because the babbling mind has an agenda and wants to control the situation because of fear and for other unknown reasons.

**The intuitive voice has few words.
The answers are simple, loving and clear.**

I had to let go of any desired outcomes and let go of what I wanted from the doctors. This meant I had to be willing to have a tooth pulled or not, to be willing to have a root canal and even orthognathic surgery.

To hear my inner voice, I needed to come from a place of no hidden desires or preferred outcomes.

One morning I was struggling with what I needed to do concerning the pain in my teeth, so I began checking in with my body. I started with "yes" and "no" questioning, as I laid very still and brought my attention to my right bottom molar. *What would be the next best step for pain relief for my upper molar?* I asked myself. *Does it need another root canal?* My body did not respond, which meant a subtle *no. Does it need to be pulled?* I received an expansive, *yes,* in my body, as my chest relaxed and opened. The word, *fractured* popped in.

I had received my intuitive answers. Then some rational thoughts followed. *But this tooth doesn't have as much pain as the others did when I had them pulled. Well screw this! I don't want to spend extra time waiting for this molar to be in intense pain or waste my money and time on extra visits. How can I bypass an appointment with Dr. Geminiz and go straight to the specialist, Dr. Gregory, to get it pulled?*

I called my root canal specialist, Dr. Geminiz and asked him about fractures. He affirmed that hairline fractures can be so small that they do not show up on x-rays. He said he would be willing to make a referral for Dr. Gregory. *Great, no extra appointments, wasting my time and money!* Within the next couple of days my tooth was pulled. Dr. Gregory said the tooth came out so easily, that there must have been an unseen hairline fracture. *Yep, just as my inner voice had said!* I thanked my inner intuition as I had saved myself more excruciating pain, money and time with the doctors.

Entering the unknown and asking deep inner questions can be emotionally unsettling and initially uncomfortable. Anxiety, fear, anger, doubt, sadness often arise while asking questions.

Sitting with emotions, validating our feelings and then talking to our hearts is an important component. In doing so, we can hear if we need nurturing, empathy or compassion. Sometimes, we may even need a good cry so the emotions can move through before addressing other Self-inquiry questions.

I would often feel sad and lonely as I had gone through three oral surgeries on my own. I was strong, but also felt isolated and vulnerable. Having pain in my mouth on a daily basis meant I was unable to chew and there were special requirements I had to adopt around eating. I was limited to soft food and had to rest a lot. I knew this was my journey and no one could do it for me. I needed to take care of myself, so I spent much of my time alone, comforting and surrendering to the pain. I would meditate and experienced great self-compassion. My chattering mind would settle and I would then ask questions about the unknown and the pain in my teeth, jaw, mouth and neck.

PERSONAL SELF-INQUIRY

What if I don't get better? I would ask myself compassionately. *You will.* My inner wisdom responded.
What if it gets worse? I continued.
It will get worse, then better. I was amazed at the clarity of response and the simple answers that passed through.
What if I have to go through this process alone? I asked with sadness.
You are never alone. Tears ran down my face.
What if there is no one to support me through my surgery?
The right people will be there to assist.
Really?
Always.

The answers brought more tears. My heart opened and I felt loved and cared for. My practice of asking and listening helped me so I wouldn't get overwhelmed with the situation and didn't feel so alone.

Often before going to doctor appointments, resistance and angst would arise in my body. Just thinking of the doctors, their authority and all their opinions, weighed me down. I felt insecure as I didn't always know what questions to ask the doctors about reducing the excess protocol around my teeth, and yet, I wanted to be seen and heard. I looked deeper and saw the negative beliefs. *They don't care about the excess paperwork, x-rays or my financial situation. They don't care about me on a personal level. They don't care or understand my intuitive knowing.* Whether any of this was true or not, it was affecting my heart and body negatively. I became nauseated and my stomach ached.

COMING BACK TO THE PRESENT MOMENT SELF INQUIRY

Are these thoughts and fears of doctors and the health care system in the present moment, past or future?
Fears of what will happen, how the doctors will treat me and if I will be able to afford all these bills are thoughts that are in the future.
What would my body feel like if I trusted this moment?
Calm and present with my body and surroundings.
What would my thoughts say if I were in this moment?
Hmm, shall I move forward, backwards, sit down, stand up, lie back down or grab my phone and call?
What would give me the greatest joy and pleasure in this moment?
Let's see; what is in this room, this home that will give me the greatest pleasure? Meditating? Writing? Movement? Brush my teeth? Call a friend? Fold laundry?
How do my body and emotions respond when I think that thought?
Open, curious, happy, excited about the possibilities. Letting go of worry.
What keeps me from being and moving from a place of self-love?
Fearful thoughts, analytical thoughts based on mistrusting myself with the doctors and fear of having a bad outcome.

What would it feel like if I knew I were loved and provided for in this moment?
Great. Relaxed. Happy.
What is keeping me from being in the moment?
Believing the negative thoughts and projecting them into the future that isn't even here yet.
Can I choose differently?
Yes.

Taking my power back, owning my choice of thoughts and choosing whether I wanted to be in this moment or not, empowered me. I could see that the negative thoughts, financial fears and stories about the doctors were useless and drained my energy.

There were other times however, even when knowing that this moment was all I had, didn't stop the fears about surgery. My mouth being punctured with anesthetic injections followed by an aggressive tooth extraction brought up fear and major resistance. My body's "fight or flight" inclination kicked in. To be so vulnerable with my body and so intimate with doctors I hardly knew brought up trust issues. *How could I surrender to someone I don't know very well?* These self-inquiry questions helped me through the most resistant and fearful times prior to surgery.

EMOTIONAL RESPONSIBILITY SELF INQUIRY

What emotion am I attaching to this situation?
Resistance.
To this doctor?
Distrust.
To surgery?
Fear
Who is putting this resistance, distrust and fear in the equation?
I am.

Who is attaching this resistance, distrust and fear to this doctor and circumstance?
I am. Well, then you can detach from the emotion and embrace it in a different way.

Can I absolutely know that this surgery, this doctor, this challenge, is *not* in my best interest? (Katie, 2002)
Not really.

What would it feel like if I embraced my resistance?
Loving and tender, soft and gentle, experiencing unconditional love.

What would it feel like if I chose to detach from the resistance completely?
Ease, effortlessness. Trust. Peace and gratitude.

What would it feel like in my body if the resistance chose to leave or was gone?
A sense of freedom, flow, receptivity.

I experimented with many self-inquiry and self-investigative questions. Some questions I made up myself and others I found in books. While experimenting with this process, I could feel into my body when there was more to ask, or when certain emotions or thoughts needed to be addressed again. Sometimes, I spontaneously began asking and other times, I went deeper into the thought process. One time I was experiencing a lot of negative thoughts and was feeling sorry for myself. I picked up Byron Katie's Book, *Loving What Is, and* began looking at what she calls "The Work."

THOUGHT EMPOWERMENT SELF INQUIRY

What thought am I putting on this situation? (Katie, 2002)
Poor me, I don't deserve this.
Is this thought helping me feel better?
No.
What thought would help me feel better?
Situations and circumstances just are. They happen to everyone.

Maybe there is something I can learn from all of this.

What might I learn from this situation?

To surrender, to have compassion and explore parts of myself not yet understood.

What would it feel like to accept this situation?

I would feel more relaxed, accepting what is and accepting my unique soul's journey.

What would I say to myself knowing that I am fully supported and loved through this situation?

This journey and this situation is perfect for my unique soul's growth. The universe is supporting me. The doctors and nurses are on my side. I can do this with love and gratitude. I am willing to learn my soul lessons and do the deep work to clear anything that is less than love, physically, emotionally, mentally and spiritually.

How do I feel when I say that to myself?

Good. Empowered. Much better.

> **As I sat there with the answers I received from my inner questioning, I began feeling a positive shift.**

My body was sensing, opening and receiving love. My mind became clear. I felt uplifted as I visualized a support group of doctors and their assistants around me. I did not know who could help me get my bite stable, but I trusted the perfect people would come when needed.

Beyond conditioning and other people's opinions, lies an inner wisdom and truth. When we have resistance, negative thoughts or emotions about our life's circumstances, we can simply inquire within. If we stop, go within, question the fear and wait for our inner wisdom to speak, the answers of truth are there. These answers are within all of us. As we learn to trust our inner voice, our intuitive body and the wisdom of our individual soul's journey, our lives became easier and we open ourselves to more self-love, power, compassion and understanding.

INNER INQUIRY QUESTIONS - PRACTICES

Do one practice a day.
If you enjoy it, circle the practice and
add it to your wellness tool box

DAY 1 PRACTICE
"Why-Not-Be-In-This-Moment?" Inquiry Process

We often unconsciously get lost in our heads (in mental activity), in the past or future, which has nothing to do with what is actually happening in the here and now. We spend our precious time analyzing and planning for situation in the future that we have no control over. We dwell on the past, playing scenes over and over in our minds. We listen and believe in fearful or judgmental thoughts and projections when we could be enjoying ourselves in the moment and trusting life as it unfolds.

These following questions will invite you back to the present so that you might become more heart centered and enjoy more of the simplicities that life has to offer in any given moment.

1. *Am I fully in my body at this moment?*

2. *What would it feel like if I trusted being in this moment?*

3. *How do my body and emotions respond when I am willing to be fully present in this moment? (It may not always be happy.)*

----

4. *What is it that keeps me from being in the present moment?*

----

5. *What would it feel like if I knew I was loved and provided for in this moment?*

----

6. *What might I choose to be doing or experiencing right now, if I truly allowed myself to be here in this moment?*

DAY 2 PRACTICE
Inner Inquiry About Negative Emotions:
Resistance, Anger and Fear

When negative emotions surface, we can freeze up, get numb or experience tension or pain in the body. We can feel disconnected to ourself and others. Fear, anger and resistance may arise in regard to certain people or challenging situations. Sometimes negative emotions flood us when unresolved issues come to the surface.

Here are some inner questions to help melt the emotional ice and shift the fear-based thought patterns around uncomfortable situations.

1. *Bring a challenging situation or person to the forefront of your mind. Name them/it.*

   _____

   _____

   _____

   _____

2. *What "negative" emotions am I attaching to this situation or to this person? Write them down (fear, anger, disgust, rage, desperate, resistance, etc.).*

   _____

   _____

3. *What story or beliefs have I attached to this person/ situation?*

   _____

   _____

   _____

   _____

4. *Is the negative emotion really happening as a result of the person/situation OR because of the story that my mind is making up? Who can let go of the story and create a new one?*

   _____

   _____

5. *Who can let go of these "negative" emotions that have been placed on this person/situation?*

   _____

   _____

6. *What would it feel like if I chose to detach these "negative" emotions from this person and situation? How would my body feel without these negative emotions towards the person or situation?*

7. *What new thoughts might I have about this person/situation so that I feel good, open and expansive?*

8. *How would I respond differently if I thought and felt that way?*

9. *How would I greet this person or walk through this situation if I knew it was perfect for me and my soul's growth? What might I do or say?*

DAY 3 PRACTICE
Listening to the Intuitive Body and Kinesthetic Testing

With the rational mind, we often go back and forth, and back and forth, as we analyze and try to figure out what is the best decision. This can be time consuming and frustrating. However, when listening to the intuitive mind and body, it is simple and precise. Developing the skills of listening to this inner knowing isn't always so easy and takes time.

In this practice, we will ask a question, then practice observing the body to get to the answers. After asking a "yes" or "no" question, if your body expands (feels open, relaxed and/or joyful), your answer is a "yes." If the body contracts (tenses, tightens and/or is unsettling), the answer is a "no." If there is uncertainty, it could be that the answer is a "maybe" and needs to be investigated further.

DIFFERENT WAYS TO USE KINESTHETIC TESTING

Experiment and see which one works best for you.

1. *If your heart expands, the answer is "yes;" if it contracts, it's a "no."*

2. *If your body feels strong, the answer is "yes;" if it feels weak, it's a "no."*

3. *If your entire body want to lean forward, the answer is "yes;" if it sways back, it's a "no."*

4. *If your arm is straight out to the side and wants to go up toward your head, the answer is "yes;" if it wants to go down toward your leg, it's a "no."*

You may want to develop your own strategies and find other kinesthetic ways that work for you.

PRACTICE WITH QUESTIONS WITH
A SMALLER IMPACT FIRST

Start with questions that won't have a big impact on your life one way or another as you learn to trust your intuitive, inner wisdom.

Here are some examples. Choose one of the kinesthetic ways of testing above and practice listening to your body with the following questions. (Keep trying out kinesthetic testing tools, until you figure out which one is best for you.)

1. *If you are getting ready to eat a banana (or other food), ask, does my body really want this? ____ Pause and listen to your body.*

2. *Shall I go to the store? (Listen for a "yes" or "no" in the body.) ____ Now? ____ Later? ____*

3. *Shall I clean my room? (Listen for a "yes" or "no" in the body.) ____ Now? ____ Later? ____*

4. *Shall I call my friend? (Listen for a "yes" or "no" in the body.) ____ Now? ____ Later? ____*

5. *Create your own yes-or-no questions below and try them out during your day.*

After you begin to trust in your body's wisdom and your intuitive, kinesthetic testing, then you can begin to ask questions that are more important and have more serious consequences.

Sometimes desire, attachment and/or emotions arise when we ask more serious questions that have more consequences. These things can make it so that we can't hear the answer right away in our body. This just means, some emotional processing needs to happen before asking the question again. When you feel clear and neutral (i.e., okay with hearing a "yes" or "no" in the body and not being attached to an outcome) ask the question again.

SECONDLY, TRY QUESTIONS WITH A BIGGER IMPACT

Here are some more serious yes-or-no questions to try.

1. *Is this relationship over?* ____ *Do I need to let them know if it is over?* ____

2. *Do I need to leave this job?* ____ *Do I need to wait?* ____

3. *Do I need to let go of this person in my life now?* ____ *Do I need to wait?* ____

4. *Is this the right place for me to move?* ____

5. *Create your own important yes-or-no questions below.*

_____

_____

_____

_____

_____

_____

Again, center and become emotionally neutral, not wanting one way or another when you ask questions. Make sure you ask questions that can be answered with "yes" or "no."

As you practice listening to your intuitive body instead of your rational mind, the voice of your body will become stronger and stronger. You intuition and heart will start to guide your life rather than your mental activity. Life will flow much easier, and your confidence will build. Listen to your body and trust your intuitive wisdom!

Chapter 8

NATURE AND HEALING VISUALIZATIONS

*"Visualization is projecting thought
energy on soul's purpose."*

ABRAHAM-ESTHER HICKS

I HAD YET ANOTHER MOLAR, MOLAR NUMBER THREE, THAT HAD similar pain issues. It was located on the bottom right. I talked to Dr. Geminez on the phone and he made the referral immediately to Dr. Gregory. The process was getting a lot easier. Dr. Geminez seemed to trust my inner knowing and realized that some of the root canals were not working and pain was still present. However, this still didn't explain why the other remaining molars were experiencing more pain as well.

During my consultation with Dr. Gregory, he agreed that the molar needed to be pulled because of the pain. He pointed out that this molar was on the bottom and my bone was thicker, so that an implant was more likely to succeed. He couldn't give me a 100% successful outcome, but reassured me as best he could. I decided to give it a try and scheduled an appointment. I had to wait a week because his schedule was so full. But he was worth it.

A few days before my oral surgery appointment with Dr. Gregory, I was working in my garden, when I came upon a large, deeply rooted weed. I tugged on it. It wouldn't come out right away. I used my shovel to dig down into its roots. It reminded me of what Dr. Gregory and the other oral surgeons may have experienced while extracting my teeth. As I pulled out the large weed, I visualized my next tooth extraction being easy, effortless and clean. I felt what it would be like to be in the doctor's shoes. I imagined his care and expertise as I pulled it out. Then I placed a geranium in the weed's spot. I smiled and was amused with the metaphor and parallel language. *Yes, the "root" of my tooth will come out easily. The im"plant" will go in easily.* I was amused by the metaphor and such clever language.

Visualizing positive outcomes using images, stories and symbols helped me stay uplifted while preparing for such aggressive procedures. It helped bring in positive energy for my mind and emotions, and my body followed suit as it relaxed and let go of tension.

The practice of visualizing the best possible outcome helped put my fears, negative beliefs and analytical thinking aside.

Positive visualizations give us feelings of well-being. So that when we actually experience the challenging event itself, we experience nearly the identical emotional and psychological effects of the positive visualizations. Chemical changes actually occur in our bodies when we use positive imageries and stories. The beneficial energetic shift is experienced in our minds first, and then translates to our bodies. Visualizing positive stories can shift our fear-based thoughts into positive ones, which can quickly bring us back into balance and into our center. (Klein, 2001)

Nature is always in balance. Nature emits light, harmony, expansion and healing energies. Visualizations of nature can help us remember our own "true nature." Nature is pure, harmonious and has no judgments or negative thinking. Nature doesn't analyze or think about the past or future, but is present in every moment.

Our projected fearful thoughts and emotions are obvious in nature because nature does not project them back to us. Nature does not resist life, but experiences all the seasons with grace, even the most stormy, chaotic conditions. We can sit in nature and reap its loving benefits because we are in fact a part of the natural world and its rhythms of constant renewal and regeneration.

I was out in my garden and noticed some negative thoughts rising. *I'm not attractive anymore. Only old people get their teeth pulled. I don't like getting old.* I pulled the weeds out of my garden one by one and saw a similar metaphor with my mind. *Hmmmm, my negative thoughts are like these weeds; I'm pulling each one out.* Then the babbling in my mind settled. *Ahhh. Plants are constantly decaying, decomposing and regenerating, just like my body.* An acceptance of my situation and of my age, with all its challenges, filled me. *Nature is in constant transition and so is my life and body. Mmmm, impermanence. Life is constantly changing.* I dug up another plant and replanted it in another spot. A deeper acceptance around my situation of growing old and losing my teeth continued to transpire.

As I rearranged the soil tenderly around another plant, I visualized my gums being soothed after my next oral surgery, then I gently placed compost around the plant's base.

I visualized my body accepting the new implant easily and painlessly. The soft way I rearranged the soil felt good. *Everything is going to be okay.* I reassured myself. *This plant, just like my im"plant," will need a little extra water and care as it re-"roots," but everything will be okay.*

Instead of pushing and resisting life's experience, we can use nature to remind us to surrender and receive love. By affirming our well-being and using positive visualizations, our perspective shifts and we are reminded of the expansive, loving, powerful energy that moves through all things. Here are some more insights, metaphors and visualizations about nature and its reminders of surrender, flexibility, centering, unconditional love, acceptance and celebrating diversity.

I desired to
SURRENDER
to life's challenges and circumstances; so I turned to the
RIVER and WIND.

A river reminds us to surrender to life's effortless flow. The flow of the river sometimes moves us fast and sometimes slowly. The river can be chaotic, and yet can be serene and silent. Life too can be filled with raging rapids of movement as well as deep, peaceful pools of stillness. Sometimes it's clear and sometimes muddy. We can practice surrendering to the river of our lives and anchor into the undercurrent of our soul's life stream. The river will melt all our obstacles of resistance on our path as we learn to surrender to it.

The wind too suggests surrender. Sometimes it gently caresses and sometimes it is turbulent and strong. We can feel the wind gently on our backs prodding us along and sometimes, it moves us with gusto, pushing us forward. The wind can powerfully break-ing trees in half and transform entire forests. The wind can blow our hearts wide open, prompting transformation. The wind also reminds us, we are not in control and that something grander is moving us. As we let go, we experience less resistance to the wind, less suffering and more inner joy. When we surrender and listen, the wind will move us effortlessly in the direction we need to go as it whispers in our ear, tickles our skin and reminds us it is safe to let go and trust.

After many checkups, consultations, various procedures and surgeries, a tight spot in my neck kept appearing. I turned to the river. The pain in my neck was like a rock. I imagined the river and wind touching this area and gently blowing and moving around it. As it softened, I visualized the pain as a gentle landslide, rolling away. As I massaged the area, a powerful "swoosh" came through and the healing river and wind energy ran through my hands. The tightness in my neck slowly dissipated into pebbles, sand and then soft mud. Remember the river and wind and their healing energy currents and remember to surrender, surrender, surrender.

I was in need of
FLEXIBILITY and CENTERING IN MY CORE
during this challenging time; I focused on the
TREES.

Trees are alive. They are stable, yet flexible, bending and always growing towards the light. Animals nest in them and people climb in and around them. All the while, trees remain stable in the core of their being. They are balanced and strong, rooted in the earth. Stormy conditions come and go and they stay centered. However, when a branch breaks, they don't complain; they just adjust. Without egos, they support our community through purifying the air we breathe, and providing shelter and food. Trees are peaceful and harmonious as they move with the wind and merge with the earth.

After seeing so many doctors with so many opinions, I turned to the wisdom of trees. I remembered to stay centered. I listened with flexibility and took what I needed, listening to my inner core and leaning toward the light. I stood secure, making decisions from a centered place, speaking my truth and yet remaining flexible as I collaborated with the doctors. Remember the trees, strong and flexible, with their peaceful, harmonious ways of being in their heart-core.

I desired
UNCONDITIONAL LOVE.
In these times of struggle and pain;
I remembered the energy of the
OCEAN.

The unconditional love of the ocean is always present. Its healing waves undulate through the water and through our cells. All rivers lead to the ocean as all paths lead to love. The unconditional love of the ocean does not refuse any of us, nor any of our situations. All of our experiences are welcomed and received as part of the greater whole. The ocean in its vastness holds everything with love and embraces the diversity in its waters.

After having so much pain and fear of the unknown, I turned to the ocean. The ocean reminded me that every step along the way, there is unconditional love surrounding me. The loving waves of energy are always pulsating through every cell of my body. I turned to this unconditional love while being with pain. I want to be like the ocean, accepting and loving the totality of my being, life and all its perfect imperfections. Remember the ocean and the deep waters of wisdom and the love that flows through everything.

I wanted to learn about
ACCEPTANCE and CELEBRATING DIVERSITY
in all paths; so I remembered the nature of
ROCKS.

There are as many shapes, colors, and types of rocks as there are people. No two rocks are the same. No two people are the same with their different backgrounds, body shapes, ethnicities, religions, interests and experiences. Yet, all rocks come from the same mother, Mother Earth. All rocks belong. Just as rocks are being molded and shaped by the elements of water and the environment, our sharp edges are always being given opportunities to be smoothed and refined by relationships and challenging situations.

I turned to the rocks. I allowed my challenging situation to polish my inner core. I was open to being shaped by the many lessons in front of me. I learned to have compassion for myself and others. I learned to accept my unique journey and its challenges. I learned to trust the polishing process of my inner stone of pain and found the gems of Self-love hidden within. Remember the stones as they remind us of the lessons and love that is in each soul's journey.

> **During the really, really painful times,**
> **the times when I had to sit or lay down to endure the**
> **pain, not knowing if it would ever stop,**
> **I would focus on my breath and visualize**
> **an angel by my side, holding my hand.**

The angel reminded me that this pain is not permanent and that nothing is permanent but the eternal love that flows through me. I would focus this light and the love of the angels surrounding me, seen and unseen.

Many of us hold varying beliefs and have had experiences with a higher source, God and master teachers such as Jesus, Buddha, angels, spirit guides or other spiritual teachers of truth. These positive images of angels, master teachers, spirit guides, nature's elementals, the light or other beings of love can helps us focus on greater healing. Visualizing light or loving beings can lift us up and help us remember that we are not alone even if no one is physically there. These visualizations and connections can comfort us and be powerful, illuminating vibrational sources of inspiration to learn on while going through challenging times.

NATURE AND HEALING VISUALIZATIONS - PRACTICES

Do one practice a day.
If you enjoy it, circle the practice and
add it to your wellness tool box.

DAY 1 PRACTICE
Knowing Your True Nature

Find an attractive nature area, the more natural the better. If this is not possible, you can use a potted plant, the sky, a tree, a piece of earth or lawn for this practice.

Take 5-10 minutes to be in the silence with the piece of nature you have chosen. See if you can refrain from going into the head and labeling things. Notice how present and alive nature is. As you gaze at nature, relax your mind and see if you can tune into the energy field that nature holds. Connect to your breath and your body's sensations and then softly gaze at nature. If your mind still wants to name and label, once again, just come back to your breath and observe with a soft gaze that which is around you. Connect with nature's pure consciousness and soothing energy vibration. Can you bring that energy into and around your own mind and body? _____ See if you can connect to your own true nature and pure consciousness. Nature will assist you.

Here are some questions to help you connect to nature and its many gifts.

1. *Who or what is nature without the mind's names and labels? You may want to repeat this question a few times and write down what comes to you.*

_____

_____

_____

_____

_____

_____

_____

2. *What can I learn from nature? See what pops in and write down your ideas.*

_____

_____

_____

_____

_____

3. *Ask yourself, who am I without my name? Without my many thoughts? Wait for a response to occur.*

_____

_____

_____

_____

_____

You may want to use this practice daily or weekly, to center and reconnect with your own true nature.

DAY 2 PRACTICE
Earth Energy Meditation-Visualization

This practice can be done in nature as a meditation or laying down in your home as a visualization.

Imagine yourself, standing or lying on the earth, with your eyes open or closed, feel the earth's energy coming up gently through your feet caressing them. Feel how the earth's energy nurtures and supports you. Notice how you feel safe with the earth's loving presence and let your guard down as much as possible.

Allow yourself to receive this energy with each breath. Pause as you take several slow, deep, nourishing breaths. As you receive nature's healing energy, watch how it relaxes your nervous system, muscles and tendons.

As you surrender and receive this energy, place your attention on a part of your body that feels tense and take a few breaths around that area. Stay present with the tension while connecting to nature's loving presence. Connect with your breath, the area in your body that is tense and nature's vibration for as long as feels right. Allow the energy in nature to move into those areas, as you let go and heal. Now feel nature's energy surrounding your entire body as you lay on the earth. Is it possible to let go even more? _____

Feel the energy of the earth moving up your legs, into your thighs and circulate in your hips. Take a breath and hold it for a couple of seconds as this loving energy fills your belly. Let nature's healing energy move up your spine and out through your arms, your shoulder and neck. Next, feel it move out the top of your head. See if your body wants to shake loose as you release. Sigh a soft "ahhhh" out loud as you release any leftover tension or anxiety in the body.

Say thank you as you bask in the earth's loving energy, doing absolutely nothing, but laying still and receiving. Continue absorbing the earth's loving energy field for as long as you enjoy.

DAY 3 PRACTICE
Unseen Helpers and Guides Visualization and Writing Activity

Imagine a loving, tender hand, reaching out to you. This hand is from one of your unseen master teachers, guides, nature elements or any other high vibrational being of love that you feel supported by. Feel their loving presence and essence of their being in front and around you. Pause for a moment; visualize and feel their pure, unconditional love for you.

They have your highest good in mind. They are whispering loving intentions in your ear right now. They have a message for you.

1. *If they could speak, what would this loving being say to you right now? Sit quietly for a while and listen. Write down what comes to you.*

   _____

   _____

   _____

   _____

2. *Imagine them placing a symbol or a loving picture above your head. What would that symbol be? Is it a specific color? What does it represent? Pause and receive*

   _____

   _____

   _____

   _____

3. *Visualize their loving hands placed on your heart. Allow yourself to receive the love. How do you feel?*

   _____

   _____

4. *Feel their embrace and their love for as long as you like. When it is time for them to go, what final words might they say to you? What comforting words do they have for you as you continue your journey in life? Write the words down if you like.*

_____

_____

_____

_____

_____

_____

Pause and take their words and love in. See them smile and remember you have their essence within you. Thank them for assisting you and know that they are with you whenever you need them and call on them.

Chapter 9

CONSCIOUS BREATH AS AN ANCHOR

*"Breath is the bridge which connects
life to consciousness, which unites
your body to your thoughts."*

THICH NHAT HANH

"OH, GREAT," I SAID SARCASTICALLY AFTER RECEIVING A PHONE call from the receptionist at Dr. Gregory's office. I found out my oral surgery had to be rescheduled and pushed back another week. I begrudgingly reminded myself, "Surrender, surrender."

The pain was intense and I wasn't in charge of the doctors and their schedules. So I used my tools to get me through. I didn't always understand where the source of pain was coming from. But I trusted my intuition. There was still pain in my other teeth, but I was addressing one tooth at a time.

**During these tough times, I relied on
my breath and gently reminded myself;**
there's nowhere to be but here.

The breath brought my focus to my body and away from the agitation I felt. Being aware of my breath also softened the painful sensations in and around my teeth, jaw and neck. Just lying in my bed and focusing on my breath became an unusual love affair with the pain and with my Self. I would send love through the breath to the pain. First noticing the sensations in my teeth, then I'd come back to my breath, then notice the sensations in my jaw and come back to my breath again. Soon I was scanning my entire body, sensing the rise and fall of my breath throughout my body.

The breathwork strategies were a doorway into the pain. I would breathe toward and into the pain while remembering the spaciousness around the pain. Then, with my mind's eye, I would turn my attention towards the deeper pockets of pain. I took deeper, longer breaths as the tightened areas in my body softened even more.

I began noticing that after ten or fifteen minutes of focusing on my breath and body, a shift would take place. It was as if a floodgate was opened and loving energy would pour through my cells. Sometimes, an utter sweetness would come over me and an emotional release of tears would follow. I was amazed at how both the intense pain and expansive, loving energy could exist at the same time. I absorbed as much of the loving energy as I could to offset the pain of the aggressive procedures I had undergone. After receiving every drop of this healing energy, feeling relaxed, centered and energized, I would get up and move forward with my life as I knew it.

> **The breath was an anchor for me to come
> back to the present moment. The breath
> reminded me to center, let go and relax.**

At last, the day arrived for my third molar to be pulled. Strangely, I was looking forward to it. I sat patiently reading a magazine while in the waiting room of Dr. Gregory's office. The receptionist and I were the only ones there. "Gerilyn," she called. His assistant ushered me into the surgery room and I took my place in the surgical chair, the same chair I sat in before. I began my breathing and affirmation practices.

Breathe in - *I am taken care of.*
Breathe out - *I let go and trust the process.*

By focusing on my breath and using positive affirmations, I was sending a positive message to my brain so that my mind and body could relax. My fears and anxiety melted, as I inhaled and oxygenated my mind and body. I began to settle in and breathe even slower and deeper receiving soothing, loving energy.

The doctor came in and sat down. "Hello, Gerilyn. Are you ready for this?"

"Yes, I am." Out of the corner of my eye, I saw some needles in his hands. Immediately my body tightened. I began focusing on my breath. *I can relax and receive for my greater good.* I stayed focused on my breath as his hands came near.

"Go ahead and open up. Just a little pinch," he said as I opened my mouth and received a few rounds of local anesthesia. My nervous system was constantly going in and out of an alarmed state because of the fear of the unknown and the doctors' invasive, aggressive procedures in my mouth. I continued to focus on my breath, slowing it down. Breathe in - *I relax and receive.* Breathe out - *I trust myself and the doctor.* It was amazing how a few deep breaths and a couple of affirmations could ground and center me, relaxing my nervous system. The doctor left the room and my mouth immediately began to get numb.

Dr. Gregory was my favorite oral surgeon. He was professional, informative, caring and known for his expertise and precision. I knew literally I was in "good hands." Even more importantly by using the breath, I could feel it.

The breath has a multitude of uses. The breath is often used as a beginning practice for meditation. The breath can be a point of reference to help when anxiety, fear, anger or chaos arise; as we learn to breathe through difficult emotions until they pass. Anger management practices use the breath as a strategy to calm oneself down by simply taking three breaths before taking any action.

The breath is used to pause in stressful moments so that we can center ourselves and make wiser decisions. Lamaze for pregnant women uses breathing techniques to help women stay focused while giving birth. Breath can also be used to enhance movements, to make them more powerful and exaggerated as in weight lifting and martial arts. With massage the breath is used as a focus to come into the body and to help loosen tight areas in the body and release tension. The breath is also used to soften slow movements as in Restorative Yoga and Chair Chi classes. Whether we focus on the breath for a minute, fifteen minutes or an hour, the breath provides the mind the opportunity to relax and let go, offering the mind and body healing benefits. The breath enhances and deepens any practice whether it be affirmations, meditation, present touch, movement or other mindfulness practices.

Dr. Gregory walked in and I knew it was time. He pulled a little on the numb side of my mouth and I couldn't feel a thing. I took a deep breath in and affirmed, *These doctors and nurses are connected to my highest good.* I breathed out, *I am connected to their Higher Self and can let go and trust this process.* Tooth number three came out with a few strong tugs. Dr. Gregory gave me a thumbs up and said "it was a little stubborn, but came out clean and the metal post for your implant is in." The assistant wiped my face and gave me some water. I was given a couple aspirin, a penicillin tablet, then scheduled a follow up appointment and was on my way home.

As soon as I got to my bedroom, I put my things down and I laid in my bed feeling exhausted. I focused on my breath and noticed my heart beating and my lungs filling up. *I am unconditionally loved at all times, no matter what I am experiencing.* The breath helped anchor the loving thoughts deeper in my body and in my heart. *I am grateful to be alive,* I affirmed. *With each breath, I am willing to receive loving, healing energy in my body.*

**I focused on the breath as I felt the loving
energy amplify throughout my body.**

The mind can try to bypass, analyze or cover up pain, but the body still holds onto it. Through longer conscious breathing sessions, it is possible to retrieve unconscious information stored in our bodies that are often hidden in the cellular structure of our muscles and tissues. By continuing to focus on the breath and the body, regardless of the thoughts, sensations and emotions that are coming up, we allow the analytical mind to take a back seat so that the unconscious can rise up to be seen and pass through. In this way, unconscious thoughts, images and stories from the past can come to the forefront to clear from our psyches and our bodies. The key is to stay connected to the breath as these old things come up and to observe them from a distance so that they can move through, without attaching to them.

One evening, I was lying in bed focusing on my breath and the sensations in my body. An image arose. I was a native American warrior standing with pride and determination. I saw myself fighting white men. Some ugly scenes of scalping a man came up too. I was angry about the men moving into our territories, dominating and aggressively taking over. I saw these images, and the feelings behind them were similar to how I felt with various doctors who were working on my teeth. It felt like an invasion in my mouth as the doctors, prodded, poked, and aggressively removed teeth. This often brought up fear and survival instincts.

By staying present with my breath, I could see the images and watch the emotions of anger along with my body's uncomfortable sensations rise, without attaching to them.

I could see from a higher level, above my analytical thinking and judgments, the emotions and images. So I could also see that the doctors had nothing to do with the images that came up. The doctors were there to help me. While focusing on my breath, I breathed through the emotions that rose up and the images soon left. New affirmations of truth were able to sink into my heart at a deeper level. My body relaxed. *The doctors are not the enemy; they are trying to help me. The doctors care about me and my well-being. I am safe.* This was a deep, deep clearing!

Later that week, I had a follow up appointment with Dr. Gregory. The surgery went well. I felt comfortable enough to talk to him about other more personal and emotional matters that often came up before surgeries. "Dr. Gregory, I sometimes have fear, anger and resistance come up before oral surgeries. My breath begins to quicken and my heart beats even faster when thinking about letting doctors in my mouth to pull a tooth. Even anger sometimes comes up." (Sometimes towards the doctors, but I didn't mention that because I knew that projection of my anger was unreasonable after the breathwork healing I received.)

Dr. Gregory sounded as if he had dealt with this before. "A fight or flight response is common with these types of procedures." The validation felt good, as I had already confronted my fears and inner warrior. He went on to say, "I try to offset the aggressiveness of the procedures with beauty and nature." Dr. Gregory pointed to a flowering plant behind a window. I liked Dr. Gregory. *Perhaps he's healing and learning some life lessons too.*

By focusing on the breath as a practice, we can ignore and let go of old beliefs, negative emotions and fears, resistance to life and past images. The unconscious rises up and is seen so that the conscious mind can release them. By honoring the unconscious and letting go, we come back into the present moment. By doing so we receive, clarity, presence, awareness, love, peace and harmony in our minds, emotions and bodies.

CONSCIOUS BREATH AS AN ANCHOR - PRACTICES

Do one practice a day.
If you enjoy it, circle the practice and
add it to your wellness tool box.

DAY 1 PRACTICE
Daily Breath Practice

This is a simple daily breath practice. Sometimes, this practice can be intense and sometimes it is just relaxing. Every breath practice will be different, depending what you are going through in that day. Stay curious. You may enjoy doing this practice in silence or put on some soothing music. Set a timer, if desired, for 5-10 minutes, so your mind can be free and doesn't have to think about time. You might also want to try a longer breathing session for 30-45 minutes. It is up to you.

Lay down or recline in a comfortable position. Place one hand on your heart and one on your belly. Focus your attention on the breath and your body. If thoughts arise, don't grasp on to them or follow them; instead say something to yourself like, "busy thoughts" or "thinking and that's okay" and then come back to your breath and the sensations in your body. If the thoughts continue (which they do, more often than not), be gentle, yet persistent and bring yourself back to the breath and body again and again.

Practice focusing on one slow, continuous breath as you trace the breath. To trace the breath, slowly inhale and notice the air coming through 1) the nostrils, 2) to the back of your throat, 3) down the throat (esophagus), 4) through the chest, 5) into the lungs, 6) through the diaphragm and 7) the belly.

Then slowly, exhale and trace the breath from 1) the belly, 2) to the diaphragm, 3) into the lungs, 4) the chest, 5) up the throat, 6) toward the back of the throat and 7) out the nostrils. Do this for a couple of minutes or longer if it feels right. Tracing of the breath will get you into your body and help you stay focused on the breath.

Energy is spreading throughout the body. Relax your focus now, let go of tracing and just observe the breath effortlessly. Watch the continuous, circular breath moving through your entire body. In other words, no pauses between the inhale and exhale.

Stay present with each inhale and exhale. That which was energetically stagnant in your body, now has an opportunity to rise and release. If emotions arise, allow them to roll on through. If intense physical sensations arise, allow them to shake loose or gently breathe through them.

(If for some reason, the sensations become too intense or the body becomes uncomfortable, just pause and relax. Get up perhaps and move so as to provide an outlet to release the tightness. Do a simple stretch or give yourself a gentle massage; anything to help move the excess energy. After that, come back to your comfortable position and settle back in with your breath.)

You may find yourself yawning, twitching, shaking or releasing in other ways too. All of these things are the body's way of letting go of tension, negative emotions and excess energy. Stay with the breath as your body releases. Keep relaxing and focusing on the breath as the energy clears. Eventually, your body will settle down again.

At the end of your session, completely let go of focusing or tracing the breath. Just allow the breath to be and flow naturally. Often a deep peaceful state of mind occurs. Allow your body and mind to recharge. Surrender into this deep relaxation. Receive all of the healing energy and insights until you feel complete.

Then ground yourself by becoming aware of the earth and how it supports your body. Try adding some small movements if you feel inspired to do so. As you open your eyes, gaze mindfully at your surroundings.

What did you release? What sensations did you experience? How do you feel now?

DAY 2 PRACTICE
Diaphragmic Breath Awareness

The diaphragm is the main muscle of respiration and is located right below your lungs and ribcage.

Close your eyes and place your hands on your diaphragm. Become aware of your hands as they rise and fall with each breath. Notice the expansion and contraction of your body with each breath. Notice how, as you inhale, the diaphragm muscle is expanding and as you exhale, the diaphragm is falling and contracting. Stay curious and engaged as you focus on this muscle.

Now take the biggest breath you've taken all day. Imagine that the diaphragm is a balloon being filled up as your hands rise. Hold the breath for two or three counts (1,2,3). Exhale slowly and then imagine the air slowly releasing out of the balloon. Do this three to seven times or whenever you feel deeply relaxed and open.

DAY 3 PRACTICE
Breath and Affirmation Integration

Using affirmations while being present with the breath can relax and re-align you mentally, emotionally and physically. Begin by reading an affirmation and then adding the breath with an inhale for the first sentence and exhale with the second sentence. Use these affirmations or make up your own.

For the Physical Body

1) *(Breathe in.) I breath in and connect to the life force energy in my body.*
   (Breathe out.) I breath out; it is safe to be present and be in my body.

2) *(Breathe in.) I accept each breath.*
   (Breathe out.) I accept my body; I accept myself.

For Emotional Well-Being

1) *(Breathe in) I accept all feelings that arise.*
   (Breathe out.) It is safe to feel and release.

2) *(Breathe in.) I breathe in love and acceptance.*
   (Breathe out.) I breathe out inner peace and joy.

For Mental Health

1) *(Breathe in.) With each inhale, I let go of all judgments towards myself and others.*
   (Breathe out.) With each exhale, I come back to love and back to this moment.

2) *(Breathe in.) I am not these thoughts, so I choose to ignore them.*
   (Breathe out.) With each breath, I come back to center, to peace and to my Higher Self.

For the Soul

1) *(Breathe in.) I am connected to unconditional love beyond all situations.*
   (Breathe out.) I go within to that still place of being.

2) *(Breathe in.) I breathe in gratitude for all my life's experiences.*
   (Breathe out.) I am willing to learn my unique soul's lessons.

Make up some of your own affirmations.

(Breathe in.)

_____

_____

(Breathe out.)

_____

_____

(Breathe in.)

_____

_____

(Breathe out.)

_____

_____

1. *Check in with yourself. How do you feel overall?*

_____

_____

2. *How does your physical body feel now?*

_____

_____

3. *What emotions are you experiencing?*

_____

_____

Chapter 10

EMOTIONAL INTELLIGENCE & QUALITY COMMUNICATION

"Love is a vibration to attune to."

PETER RENGEL

I LEARNED TO TALK AND LISTEN TO THE PAIN AS I WOULD A FRIEND. I became a good listener. To hear my body's needs, I gave it deep presence without disruption. I needed to give the pain in my body the same attention a baby or young child needs from its mother. I learned to listen to it with patience and acceptance. The pain became a very intimate ally. The same listening and communication tools I used with my body, I also used with the people that I love.

Hello pain, what are you needing? Are you needing gentleness? I asked with an empathetic ear.

Are you needing sweet love and acceptance just as you are? My body responded with an affirmative *Ahhhh. Yes, that's it.* As I gave presence to any discomfort I felt, the contracted area began to relax. My nervous system settled down and my muscles softened.

Sometimes words came to me as if the pain was speaking. I listened carefully to its specific requests and guidance. *Send loving energy to the right bottom tooth. Gently massage around the edges.* I was patient and slow, giving my gums and jaw as much of this loving attention as it needed. When enough love had been received, the area would relax with satisfaction. The interaction was complete and I would go onto the next part of my body.

I gave the area in my mouth where the teeth had been pulled attention. Deep sadness rose up. I had gone through so many aggressive procedures and surgeries, having three teeth and a failed implant removed. A much-needed cry surfaced. Before I could completely and totally accept the new circumstances surrounding my mouth, I needed to grieve. Like a good friend, I held the container for as many tears as wanted-to-be-expressed.

There were other times, I would give my teeth attention, finding myself impatient and trying to fix the pain. I would try to make the pain go away instead of listening to what it really needed. I would experience frustration and then a wall of resistance as my body would buckle up and get tighter. If the pain had words, it would be saying "Slow down. Stop trying to push the healing process faster than it wants to go. Stop trying so hard and let me heal slowly in my own time." *Oh yes, this makes sense, this is healthy communication, listening and not pushing and trying to force my agenda.* I would then energetically pull back and listen carefully to the pain while giving it tender attention.

We don't always have healthy communication skills with our bodies. Most of us haven't been taught or shown how to be present and listen, or how to identify deeper desires and give what is really needed. Almost all of us have inherited unhealthy ways of connecting to our bodies, emotions and minds.

We haven't learned how to listen to negative emotions with ourself and to see the need behind the emotion. There is so much dysfunction in the ways we communicate as children and adults. Instead of identifying our negative emotions and automatically turning toward the need behind it, we often blame or project our negative emotions onto others and the world at large.

Instead of knowing our needs and directly asking for what we want, we often are passive aggressive, avoiding, being sarcastic, gossip and make others wrong.

The majority of us have been shown unhealthy ways of communicating since childhood from our primary care takers, television and society as a whole. As we go through life though, we can heal the generational dysfunction that was passed on to us. Our parents did the best they could with the communication and intimacy skills that were handed down to them. Now we can learn new ways to communicate with ourselves and each other. We can shift the unhealthy, dysfunctional communication styles we might have learned into ones that are authentic, loving, clear and direct. In this way, we heal and let go of unhealthy, "poor me'" victim roles, angry perpetrator roles and co-dependent, enabling rescuer roles. (Bradshaw, 1990) (Beattie, 1987)

> **When intense pain arose, I found it difficult to say "no" to people close to me. I found myself beating around the bush instead of being direct.**

The subtle ways I wasn't being true to myself and the codependent ways of sacrificing my needs stared me in the face. I realized there were some areas where I was not used to making my own well-being the first priority. My pain, however, forced me to address these areas; I had to listen to my body and give it 24/7 attention. I felt guilty at first and was afraid I'd lose people's love if I made myself a priority. This guilt was very subtle. I had an unhealthy core belief. *Making myself my number one priority all the time is selfish.* But I had no choice. The pain spoke loudly and constantly. The pain in my mouth, teeth and neck demanded I give it attention before anyone else. The pain was too great to ignore. Because of the pain, I had very little energy to give to anyone. And when I did have energy, I never knew for how long or when I would need to take a break and lay down because of the pain. Therefore, I couldn't commit to any activity 100%.

I love and adore my daughter who lived a couple hours away from me. I love being someone she can count on when she is making important life decisions. She was 26 at the time and looking for an apartment near the University that she would be attending the next few years. She asked if I might come join her and scope out some of the houses and apartments near the University. My mothering heart right away said "Yes, I can help you look." It took every ounce of energy I had to drive 50 miles to where she was staying. I pushed myself to be there through the pain. I was determined. I pulled over several times off the highway to rest. When I got to the place she was staying, I was exhausted.

There was too much pain in my body to go looking for an apartment the next morning. I didn't know how to communicate this because I wasn't used to always putting my needs first, especially with my daughter. I tried to push myself to get ready to go apartment hunting, but I couldn't; the pain was too much. I felt frustrated. Beneath the frustration, I felt sad and guilty for not being able to go with her.

> **I was frustrated and confused not knowing how to make myself first and not knowing how to ask for what I really needed.**

"When will you be ready to go, Mom?"
"I don't know," I would reply as I was laying down, being with the pain.
"Well, I'm ready, so let me know when you are."
Sadness would come, because I didn't know when the pain would go away and didn't want her to wait or tell her "No I can't go."
"Mom, can you give me an estimated time?"
"I would like to go but I don't know when," I replied. Tears came down. I didn't know how to respond and when I did, it was confusing.
"Do you want me to wait for you?" she asked in a calm voice.
"I don't know when I will feel better, but I would like to go." I was repeating myself. "I just don't know."

She became frustrated. "Mom, what are you trying to say?"
I spoke with hesitation. "I want to go. I just don't know if I can."
She continued to ask for clarity. "Okay, will you eventually tell me?"
I answered with a distraught tone of voice, "I don't know. I'm still in pain and don't know when it will end." The frustration and tension built. I was up against a hurdle.

**My confusion and indirect communication
put us at odds with each other and yet,
all I wanted was to connect.**

To my credit, I wasn't blaming her or attacking her. I was just confused and didn't know how to communicate what I really needed. And To my daughter's credit, she was being incredibly patient, kind and clear.

I wanted her to read my mind.

I wanted her to wait for my body to feel better even though I didn't know how to communicate this to her clearly and directly. Lovingly, she sat with me through all my frustration and confusion. I went to lie on the couch in the other room to go inward and feel my sadness. I looked at my desire to take care of her needs at the expense of my own and my lack of clear communication. I wanted her needs to be met, as this was the only day she had to go searching for apartments.

I was afraid to say, "No, I can't go right now." As I owned my fears, I took a closer look behind my behavior. In doing so, I noticed conditioned beliefs. *She won't love me if I say "no." If I say "no," it means I don't love her.* I also had a fear that I had nothing to offer, but presence. Thoughts of not being worthwhile or a good mother brought tears. I wanted to say "no" and yet be honest, vulnerable and communicate clearly what was really going on inside, so that we could stay connected.

The pain finally settled a little. I got up off the couch and approached my daughter while she was tidying up in the kitchen. She turned around as I walked toward her. "Honey, can we try that conversation again?"

**"May I do a 'redo'? I'd like to practice
communicating my needs and making a clear request.
Are you open to that?" I asked.**

She was, so I began. "Honey, I'm not able to go right now and don't know when I will because I need to take care of my body. Don't wait for me, 'cuz I don't know when the pain will go away completely or when it will come back. I know I told you I would drive and help out. I'm afraid all I have to offer right now is presence. I love you and wish I could be there for you and it makes me sad I can't go with you right now in the way I was hoping to." This lesson of making myself a priority was being taken to a whole new level. My inner listening and needs had to come first, even with my girl.

**I was discovering my subtle, co-dependent
habits and practicing new, healthy ways
of communicating directly.**

She was disappointed and yet her response was compassionate. "Mom, of course I want you to go with me and if you can't, you can't. I'll finish up my breakfast and clean up. If you are in a different space then, let me know."

The funny thing is, after she was done eating and cleaning up, the pain had subsided. "Honey, I can go now. Would it be okay if I don't drive and sit in the passenger's seat, just in case my pain rises?"

"Of course."

This was surely a growing time, making my needs first while desiring that others needs be met as well. I was learning and practicing new ways of communicating while shifting old, codependent beliefs into new, healthy beliefs. *It is okay to make my own well-being a priority.*

> **Was it really okay to make myself that much of a priority? Was it really okay to ask for what I really wanted or needed in every moment?**

These questions pushed the self-love envelope even further. These were questions I asked myself as I embraced the pain and deepened my ability to listen to my moment to moment needs. I often did not fully ask for what I really wanted, nor did I completely trust my gut instinct when my inner guidance spoke up.

What keeps us from asking for what we need and want 100% of the time? Here are some of the reasons I came up with. See if they hold true for you.

1. We believe it is not polite to put our needs first. "It is better to give than to receive."

2. We often don't know what our needs are or what to ask for.

3. We've been raised to think that other's needs are more important than our own.

4. We feel unworthy and insecure, so we don't give our self permission to ask for what we want 100% of the time.

5. We are afraid we might hurt someone's feelings and then feel guilty.

6. We are afraid of conflict and of being rejected or abandoned.

7. We are fearful others might say "no" if we ask.

8. We are even more afraid of what we will tell our self what the answer "no" means. (Bryson, 2002)

I also noticed my fear of asking for what I wanted with doctors. After all, they are the ones who are supposed to have the answers, right? They are supposedly the authorities on health. But, I was the only one who really was familiar with my body day to day. I was the one who spent hours listening to it. I was the only one who was looking out for my financial situation. I learned to listen to my body, emotions and ask directly for what I needed.

I learned to listen carefully in order to prevent myself from having months of further pain or having to make excess trips to the doctor. However, despite all I had been through, yet another tooth was beginning to show the same signs as the other three that had already been pulled. Even though I had anxiety, I called Dr. Geminiz to tell him of the situation and about the pain in yet another tooth. I told Dr. Geminiz and he gave me a referral right away for Dr. Gregory. I practiced using the following basic steps for inner reflection and quality communication. Because of this, I was saved hours of frustration and confusion with myself and with the doctors. These five steps empowered me in my journey with my body, with the doctors and all my relationships.

FIVE SIMPLE STEPS FOR QUALITY COMMUNICATION -

1. IDENTIFY "NEGATIVE" EMOTION.

2. IDENTIFY NEED.

3. MAKE A LOVING, DIRECT REQUEST.

4. LOOK FOR A WIN-WIN.

5. LOVINGLY COMMUNICATE "NO THANK YOU," IF THERE IS NO WIN-WIN.

(Rosenberg, 2003)

It is important to know your emotions, to be able to identify the needs behind the emotions and to be able to ask for what you want without demanding. Sometimes, there is no solution after creatively negotiating. Both parties have tried their best to create a win-win, but they can't because one of them would be giving in instead of being true to themselves. Under this circumstance, a compassionate "no deal" is in order. The following steps can help individuals get their own needs met while at the same time, supporting beloved friends, lovers, co-workers and family members to get their needs met too. These steps can work with anybody and any situation. (Rosenberg, 2003)

1. FIRST IDENITIFY ANY "NEGATIVE" EMOTION WITHOUT JUDGING YOURSELF OR OTHERS.

Stay away from repeating the story or judgments about the situation or person and focus on what you are feeling (not what you are thinking). Negative feelings remind us that something isn't quite right. Positive emotions on the other hand are a result of getting our needs met. When we check-in with ourselves and see what we are feeling, we can then validate our "negative" feelings, such as anger, frustration, confusion, spaciness, irritation, sadness and so on. We can begin to discover that behind every "negative" emotion lies an unmet need. It is important we learn to sit with the "negative" emotions we feel without projecting them onto others. Projection only perpetuates drama and when there is drama, we risk the possibility of disconnecting from those we care about and create more stress for ourselves. The key is to identify and be with the "negative" emotion in a healthy way, either alone or perhaps with a friend who is able to hold a safe space until we are able to identify the emotion and perhaps the need behind it. Then we can re-center, as we get ready to make simple requests in a healthy way.

EXAMPLE: I sat by myself before going into surgery and noticed I was fidgety. My nerves were on edge and I was experiencing some negative feelings. *What am I feeling?* "Ah. I am feeling afraid and nervous about the surgical procedure."

2. THEN IDENTIFY THE NEED BEHIND THE NEGATIVE FEELING.

Marshal Rosenberg identifies several needs that we all have in common: 1) Food and shelter, 2) Honesty and integrity, 3) Community and support, 4) Purpose and meaning, 5) Play and expression, 6) Clarity and awareness, 7) Autonomy and choice, 8) Empathy and intimacy, 9) Nurturing and touch, 10) To be seen and appreciated and 11) Inner peace and compassion (Rosenberg, 2003. Charde', 2006). It is extremely important not to make any one person or thing responsible for meeting all our needs. Besides, that is an impossible task. If we expect all our needs to be taken care of by one person, we can become resentful and demanding when that person is not interested or unavailable to meet our needs. Resentments, in turn, create distance which can ultimately push people away, creating uncomfortable situations and deep rifts in relationships.

EXAMPLE: *What need is behind my nervousness, anxiety and fear?* "I have a need for comfort and nurturing during surgical procedures so I can relax, feel at ease and be receptive to the extraction."

3. AFTER BRAINSTORMING STRATEGIES TO GET YOUR NEED MET, MAKE A SIMPLE, ATTAINABLE REQUEST.

There are many ways to get our needs and desires met. Brainstorm with yourself or others different ways and strategies for you to get your needs met. Keep an open mind so that if one strategy doesn't work, you can try another. Depending on the situation and the person, we may choose to ask the person to help us in getting a need met, or we may choose to get it met in another way. However we get our needs met, making simple requests will give us a better chance of getting our needs and wants met in relationships. It also gives us a better chance of maintaining and deepening close connections with the people involved.

Make sure you are requesting and NOT demanding. A great indicator that we are making a request and not a demand is our receptivity to hearing "No." If we check within and notice there is no resistance to hearing the response of "No" to what we have asked for, then most likely our asking is indeed a request. If we get upset, frustrated or angry hearing a "No" to our request, most assuredly it is a demand. Remember, there is no ONE person who can meet all your needs. It is important to be creative and trust that the universe has many ways for you to get your need met.

EXAMPLE: Two strategies and requests I used with the doctor's assistants in order to get my needs of nurture and comfort met in the surgical room.

"Would you be willing to play some softer, gentler music? I'm needing nurturing during the surgeries and would really appreciate it."

"I'd like to bring my own pillow and padding for extra comfort. Would that be okay?"

4. IF NEEDED NEGOTIATE A WIN-WIN SO BOTH INDIVIDUALS CAN GET THEIR NEEDS MET.

Sometimes our requests get met right away with a resounding "Yes!" The request to bring my own pillows in for comfort and support was such. It isn't always that easy however. Sometimes we need to brainstorm independently with ourselves or collaboratively with others. Sharing creative strategies will often help us find ways to get our needs met and help us negotiate with others so they can get their needs met too. I asked for softer, more soothing music in one doctor's office and they said "No, the station can't be changed." I gave them empathy and then attempted to negotiate. This is how that conversation went.

EXAMPLE: "I understand you aren't able to change the station." Then I made another request with a different strategy. "Would it be possible to bring in my own music and play it on my own musical device?" The response was, "Sure that will work."

5. LASTLY, SOMETIMES IT IS JUST NOT POSSIBLE TO GET BOTH INDIVIDUAL'S NEEDS MET TOGETHER AND A COMPASSIONATE "NO THANK YOU," IS IN ORDER.

The highest expression of getting two individuals' needs met can end in a "no thank you" agreement. A "no thank you" agreement simply means that we are not willing to go against our inner core happiness and meet another person's needs at the expense of our own. There were times when I knew a doctor or dentist would not be able to listen and collaborate with me. I chose not to continue to see those doctors. I had tried several times to communicate my needs and made direct requests, and my needs were not attended to. Settling for less would have compromised my core desire to find doctors who would collaborate with and listen to me. Life is too short not to enjoy and create a life of harmony and joy when we can.

EXAMPLE: I quit seeing Dr. Black. This is what I said to his assistants at the front desk. "Thank you for your services. I have found another doctor who I will be working with. Would you please send my x-rays to Dr. Gregory?"

No one can meet our needs 100% of the time, but we can always ask. There is only one place to find love 24/7, and that place is within our own hearts. Love is a vibration that we can connect to at any moment and at any time no matter what the circumstance. That's why love is a choice. Even in pain and suffering, love can be present. Deep inside, we all yearn for intimacy, to be seen and to witness others at a heart and soul level. Yet there is only one connection we will always have in every moment in all of our life, and that is with our self. So why not learn loving, inner communication? We cannot be truly successful and satisfied in our relationships if we don't become familiar with and love all dimensions of our self.

EMOTIONAL INTELLIGENCE, NEEDS AND QUALITY COMMUNICATION - PRACTICES

Do one practice a day.
If you enjoy it, circle the practice and
add it to your wellness tool box.

DAY 1 PRACTICE
The FOUR Daily Questions:
1)Feelings, 2)Needs, 3)Brainstorming Strategies, 4)Making Requests...
and SOMETIMES Negotiating and No-Deal

CHECK IN WITH YOURSELF THROUGHOUT THE DAY WITH THE FOL-
lowing FOUR questions. If you do this inner inquiry process often
enough, you will develop new thought patterns and behaviors when
dealing with negative emotions and addressing your inner needs
and values. Instead of projecting outwardly, blaming, gossiping,
being loud and demanding, shutting down, avoiding and ignoring,
using put downs, being sarcastic, having physical violence and other
passive aggressive behaviors, you simply go within and identify your
needs and ask for what you desire. It is simple, but not always easy
because of our conditioning and past programming. There are many
ways to get needs and desires met. And when our needs are met, we
return to a sense of well-being satisfaction, peace and happiness again.

1. *EMOTIONS: How am I feeling in this moment? In gen-*
   eral, if you are feeling positive, no more inquiry is needed.
   That is because when you feel good, your needs are already
   met. For the sake of practice however, even if you are feeling
   positive, think of a situation, a person or time when you
   were experiencing a negative emotion.

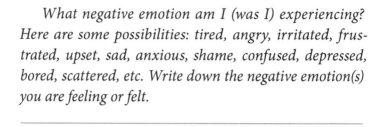

*What negative emotion am I (was I) experiencing?
Here are some possibilities: tired, angry, irritated, frustrated, upset, sad, anxious, shame, confused, depressed,
bored, scattered, etc. Write down the negative emotion(s)
you are feeling or felt.*

_____

_____

2. ***NEEDS/DESIRES/VALUES: What need (or desire) that
   you have is/was NOT getting met?*** *When we experience
   a negative emotion, it simply means there is a need not
   getting met. It is up to us to redirect inward and figure out
   what the need is, so we can focus on getting it met.*

   *Identify the need (or desire) now. Here are some pos-
   sibilities: appreciation, freedom, honesty, respect, support,
   purpose, play, freedom, quiet time, clarity, choice, empathy,
   nurture, inner peace, harmony, connection, sustenance,
   etc. (Rosenberg, 2003). Write your answers down here.*

   _____

   _____

3. ***BRAINSTORMING STRATEGIES: Can I easily give this
   need to myself right now?*** ___ *If it's a yes, great, then give
   it to yourself; no need to go any further.*

   a. *If NOT, brainstorm other strategies to get your needs
      met. (You can brainstorm with a conscious friend too!)
      There are many strategies and ways to get our needs met.
      It is very important though, to refrain from any sort
      of demand that your needs get met in ONE particular
      way, or by ONE particular person. Be willing to explore
      all possible strategies. This can open the door to getting
      your needs met in ways you never thought possible and
      from sources you may never have considered!*

b. *What kinds of activities or actions could you take to get your needs met?* Write down ALL the possible strategies to get your needs met that could work for you.

_____

_____

_____

_____

_____

If one of these strategies works for you and you don't need to make any requests, great, circle it. If not, you may need to ask someone to help you get this need met; go to #4 MAKING REQUESTS.

4. **MAKING REQUESTS: What request to others will you make to get your need(s) met?** When you make a request, be loving, direct and clear. Be very careful on your wording here, as some times we can slip into old patterns of guilting, apologizing, "shoulding," insisting or other passive aggressive tendencies. Here are some starters.

a. "Are you willing to _____?"

b. "Would you be interested in _____?"

c. Write down some requests you could make regarding the situation/person.

_____

_____

_____

_____

_____

Basically, if you aren't willing to hear an answer of "no," it is a demand not a request. However, sometimes they are saying "no" because their needs aren't being met but if you negotiate with them so their needs can be met, you may be able to get your needs met too. If this is the case, go to NEGOTIATING.

Sometimes, you may sense or know that you just can't get your needs met with this person or situation; i.e., too much work, not available, they aren't interested, etc.; sometimes it's best to go elsewhere. Go to NO-DEAL.

NEGOTIATING: *Sometimes, it is important to negotiate for a win-win for both parties, so both of your needs are met. When you realize, the other person was just trying to get their needs met too and that is why they were a "no," you might be able to identify their needs as well and negotiate. In this way, you can negotiate and find a possible win-win so both of your desires and needs get met. What do you think the other person's need(s) may have been?*

_____

_____

_____

_____

_____

a. *"Oh, I see that wouldn't work for you because of your need for _____. Well, 1 I have a need for _____. So, instead, maybe we could do it at a different time or place, etc. Would that work for you?*

b. *"Or maybe I could _____ instead which would help give you _____. What do you think?"*

c. *How might you negotiate so both your needs can get met?*

Brainstorm with the other person until you come up with an agreement that meets both of your needs. If this can't be done. Go to NO-DEAL.

NO-DEAL: *And sometimes, it is just a "no-deal," where you've tried all the negotiations to get both of your needs met and it just won't work. Both of you just aren't satisfied. This is actually a very high level of loving communication and commitment to oneself and to each other's well-being. How might you communicate a "no-deal." Here's some ideas.*

a. *"Hey, I wish this could work out, but I can't meet your needs in this situation. I'm sure you will find some other place (or person)."*

b. *"This just isn't going to work for me. I hope you understand."*

c. *Write some of your own "no-deal" communications.*

These FOUR questions, and sometimes NEGOTIATING and NO-DEAL practices, will help you remember to go within to listen to your negative emotions and identify your needs behind them without projecting them on to others. In this way, you will have more harmonious and "needs" satisfying relationships. It is important to do the inner work when a negative emotion arises and eventually bring these skills out into REAL TIME. Be gentle with yourself as you take steps towards Self-mastery. With enough practice, you will begin to experience more authentic, harmonious and satisfying relationships. (Rosenberg, 2003)

DAY 2 PRACTICE
Bringing the FOUR Daily
Questions to Others with Empathy

You can use the same FOUR questions above to situations regarding others' negative reactions and emotions. By practicing these questions, you can often bring order to chaotic situations, stay connected to the individual you are trying to relate to and create more harmonious relationships.

This practice has two parts. First, learn to go within and do some INNER COMPASSIONATE REFLECTION around other's negative emotions and behaviors. This will help you shift your old reactive ways of thinking and behaving when you see others who are experiencing negative emotions and reacting. Secondly, you will learn how to use these same skills in REAL TIME with others which is truly satisfying. In this way, you will help them identify their negative emotions, their needs and brainstorm ways for them to get their needs met (along with your needs too.)

Of course, if someone is not interested in owning their negative emotion or behavior, and wants to keep blaming, complaining, using sarcasm, is into drama and being passive aggressive, and so on, you may need to distance yourself from these relationships. Then focus on finding friends and family members who are interested in practicing emotional intelligence and quality communication.

INNER COMPASSIONATE REFLECTION

Think of a person or situation in your mind (a child, friend, family member or partner) that had a negative emotion and was blaming, accusing, gossiping, attacking and projecting a negative emotion outward on to you or others. And then do the FOUR questions.

1. **FEELINGS: Can you guess what emotion they may have been experiencing in that situation?** *Were they feeling fearful, hurt, unsure, confused, shame, frustrated, angry, disappointed, sad, etc.? Write it down.*

   _____

   _____

2. **NEEDS: Can you guess the need they might have had behind the negative emotion they were experiencing?** *Perhaps they were needing to feel safe, to be loved, respected, understood, validated, listened to, to be seen, appreciated, to play, or they are needing honesty, clarity, trust, freedom, harmony, peace, justice, intimacy, nurturing, quality communication, etc. Write down what need you think they had in that moment.*

   _____

   _____

3. **BRAINSTORMING STRATEGIES: Now that you've guessed their need behind the negative emotion, brainstorm and guess how you might help them get their need met.** *(Not at the expense of others or your own needs of course.) Write down some of the possibilities.*

----

4. **REQUEST GUESSING: *Can you create a question that gives them a strategy to getting their need met?*** *We do this because, usually, they aren't able to make a request because they don't know their needs and how to take that next step. You can help them out with the next step. After you've done the inner work of identifying their need and brainstormed strategies for them to get their needs met, create a question that provides a strategy to get their need met. Here are some examples.*

   a. *"Are you needing me to be present and just listen, instead of tell you about my experience?"*

   b. *"Would you like me to slow down so you can feel safe while I'm driving?"*

   c. *"Next time, I will wait to talk to you instead of interrupting your conversation. Would that be helpful?"*

   d. *Create some of your own "Request Guesses" regarding the situation.*

NEGOTIATING: *If needed, after you have let the other person know you are willing to help them get their needs met, negotiate to get your needs met as well. How might you negotiate a "win-win" in that situation so your needs get met too?*

a. "I am willing to do _____ so you can get your need met of _____.

b. Would you be willing to do _____, so I can get my need of _____ met?"

c. What words would you use to negotiate?

_____

_____

_____

If they aren't interested in getting your needs met, it may be time to move forward to "No-Deal."

NO-DEAL: *Make sure that you do NOT meet someone else's needs at the expense of your own. You aren't responsible for meeting anyone's needs (unless they are a baby or child of course who you are responsible for and who is dependent on you). Adults can find many ways to get their needs met.*

a. "Unfortunately, I just can't do that, as it takes away from my freedom. I'm sure you'll find someone else."

b. "It's really not my thing. But thanks for asking."

c. If it's a "No-Deal," what would you say to the person?

_____

_____

REAL TIME QUALITY COMMUNICATION

Now let's look at what to do if the situation is happening in REAL TIME. If someone is standing in front of you, displaying negative emotions or behaviors, the process is no different. The questions are lovingly directed towards them in REAL TIME. These skills take

time to acquire, so be gentle on yourself as you continue to do the
INNER COMPASSIONATE REFLECTION practices, progressing
towards REAL TIME.

1. **FEELING: Guess the emotion.**
   "Sounds like you might be feeling _____?" (angry, sad, upset,
   shame, irritated, etc.) Keep guessing the emotion until they say
   "Yes, I am feeling that way."

2. **NEEDS: Then identify the need behind the negative**
   emotion.
   "Are you needing _____ right now?" (presence, someone to
   listen, to be heard, validation, love, appreciation, honesty,
   integrity, connection, sustenance, understanding, support, etc.)
   *   Once again keep guessing until you hear "Ahhh, yes, that's*
   it," or "No, it's not that. It's this _____." Whether you
   figure out the need or they do, it doesn't matter, the focus is
   on identifying the need.

3. **BRAINSTORM STRATEGIES: What possible strategies**
   might they use to get the need met?
   In your mind, think of some possible strategies to help them
   get their needs met in that very moment. These strategies may
   involve you rephrasing or rewording something, giving presence
   or listening, or moving a chair, holding a hand, etc. This will
   all depend on what their need is.

4. **REQUEST GUESSING: Guess what their need is and**
   guess a strategy to get that need met.
   Here are some ideas. "Sounds like you are needing _____.
   Would you like me to _____? Would
   it be helpful if I _____?"
   *   They may say "yes" or "no" but eventually, together, you*
   may come up with something that would work for them to get
   their need met. Of course, if getting their needs met infringes
   upon your need, you may need to NEGOTIATE.

NEGOTIATING: *Because they may not think about your needs, as they don't even know their own needs, you may need to negotiate, so that your needs are met too.*

"Let's see. I also have a need, which is _____. Let's meet your needs first by _____, then mine by _____. Does that work for you?"

They may have some other ideas as you negotiate and brainstorm together. If they are not willing to consider your needs, a "No-Deal" may be in order.

NO-DEAL: *If it's not possible to meet their needs in that moment and yours at the same time, a "No-Deal" will allow everyone to get their needs met and go their own ways, hopefully, in a loving way.*

"I understand, you want _____ but it's not going to work for me at this time. I just don't see any way around it. Thanks for trying to negotiate though."(Rosenberg, 2003)

Dr. William Glasser states "Every behavior is one's best attempt at getting a need met." The behavior isn't always the best for everyone involved, but we are all just trying to get our needs met. With this understanding, we can at least have compassion for all humans. And also help each other find strategies and solutions that are a "win-win" for everyone.

Be gentle with yourself and others as you learn and practice together. Emotional awareness and quality communication are a life-long practice that will bring more joy, satisfaction and depth for your own life and to all your relationships.

DAY 3 PRACTICE
Ask for a "Re-Do" to Improve Your
Everyday Relationships and Communication

Most of us haven't been taught emotional intelligence skills and quality communication. We don't always use loving, empowered communication and requests. Therefore, detecting and monitoring negative emotions and going inward (instead of outward), looking to see what our needs are and lovingly making requests, is a life-long practice.

The "Re-Do" is a great practice to clean up relationships after we realize we were projecting our emotions outward towards someone. We let the other know that we are practicing quality communication and would like to practice using more loving, direct ways to communicate. We may want to apologize and then start the "Re-Do" process.

We simply begin by asking:

"Hey, I'm practicing quality communication and emotional intelligence. Would you be open to me doing a 're-do' of that past conversation? What I said didn't land quite right."

An example: A girlfriend uses her cell-phone when you are with her at a resort where no cell-phones are allowed. You don't say anything, but it really bothers you because you want to get away from all the electronics.

You make a sarcastic, yet, playful statement instead of asking directly for what you want. "Using your phone again huh? Can't get away from it can you? Are you ever going to turn that thing off?"

She answers you with a snarled expression and snaps back, "Whatever. I've got an important phone call to make." You notice the disconnect and awkwardness between the two of you. You sit there for a while with the tension that is not being addressed. You realize there was a hint of sarcasm behind your statement. Then you realize, I could do a "re-do."

First things first. It's time for you to go within and do inner reflective work before addressing the disconnect. (Reminder: The "Re-Do" method is never about the other person doing it differently. But about you being empowered and improving your skills. You will be amazed at when you shift, the connection shifts.)

1. **NEGATIVE EMOTION:** *Identify when you FIRST felt the negative emotion in your body. _____ In the example*

above, it was when your friend used her cell-phone with you in the vicinity.

2. **NEEDS:** *What need did you have? _____ In the example above, the need was simply, silence and getting away from it all.*

3. ***BRAINSTORMING STRATEGIES:*** *The strategy to get your need met was to turn off all electronics. There are other strategies that could work also. Since her needs are to be able to communicate with others, see if you can brainstorm other strategies that might meet both of your needs, for a win-win. Perhaps, your friend could get their needs met by finding places that are not in your vicinity, away from you, to make their phone calls. In this way both your needs can be met, you receive silence and getting away from electronics and her need to connect to others is also met.*

4. ***MAKING REQUESTS:*** *The "re-do" will be to directly ask for your needs to be met instead of being sarcastic. Now that the inner work has been done with deeper self-reflection, time for a "re-do" request.*

It would go something like this:
   "Hey, may I do a 're-do?' I realize I wasn't using quality communication. I would like to practice my skills so I can improve and ask for my needs lovingly and care about your needs as well." *It is important to take responsibility for your side of the reacting and let them know you expect nothing from them. Stay focused on your "re-do," not theirs. Of course, if they are interested, in Quality Communication, they may naturally join in. Just by you doing the "re-do," it will shift everything. Also, if they aren't available in that moment for a "re-do," then set up a time with them to do your "re-do" at a later date. Now, time to go back to the conversation where you became a little sarcastic, defensive or reactive and wipe out everything you said.*

"I'd like to start at the beginning of the conversation right when *you pulled out your cell-phone and made a call. Are you open to* *that?"* Most likely, they'll say "yes" if you are sincere.

"Hey, I notice you are using your phone. I was wondering if *you would be willing to use your phone when I'm not around?* *I'm really needing silence and wanting to get away from all the* *electronics."* Most likely their response would be "sure" because you are honoring their need to connect and make phone calls, and your need for silence and getting away from electronics is being met also.

Yea, both your needs are getting met for a win-win. Now, if they say "no" to a "re-do," accept that and do it with yourself so you can improv your Emotional Intelligence and Quality Communication skills.

Chapter 11

INNER RHYTHMS AND AUTHENTIC MOVEMENT

"Movement gives us a window to that which is rooted in energy not judgment. It is a language where we can communicate with ourselves as energy."

GABRIELLE ROTH

IT WAS FRIDAY IN THE AFTERNOON AND I WAS GRATEFUL TO HAVE the weekend off to relax deeply and heal. Oral surgeries were averaging about once every two to three months. The time in between was spent going to follow up appointments and nurturing the pain. I had no choice but to slow down and take time to integrate all that was happening in my life and body.

I laid motionless in bed with little to no energy. I wondered if the thread of life force energy that had been moving me all my life was still there. Years prior to all of this, I enjoyed practicing something called "authentic movement," a simple form of inner exploration involving spontaneous, self-directed movements and stillness while being in the present moment. I practiced authentic movement at ecstatic dances and other authentic movement workshops, but now there was no movement here. While lying in my bed, I recalled one of my teachers saying that the effortless flow rhythm is always there, even in silence and stillness.

**The pain and sensations in my body kept
pointing me to stillness, *inner silence,* a rhythm I was
accustomed to when I went to bed or
took short meditative naps. But I had never explored so
much inner silence as this.**

The constant pain kept pointing me inward and the sensations in my body were my focus. I would lie there for hours soothing myself, waiting patiently for movement to come.

This was an unusual gift. As I watched all the mental activity settle, loving energy entered and my physical body began to surrender and relax. I nurtured the pain and my inner self deeply as I focused on my breath. To the common eye, it may have looked as if I was a bit depressed, but I wasn't. I had become fascinated with the edges of this healing life force energy and listening to my inner rhythms just as they were. Everything was shifting but the rhythms were still there; a bit slower, but still there. I laid there receiving love, observing and waiting for the next undercurrent to move me.

Besides, there wasn't much to do anyway. My daughter was raised and doing well. I didn't have a boyfriend or man in my life. My job being a nanny was simple and my nanny-boy was getting older, so he didn't need as much help. All I had was some book ideas that kept popping in my mind, *Inner Physician.* I liked the idea as I had a compilation of healing strategies that I was using to get through this difficult time. However, with my energy being so low, I could let those ideas go for now.

Sometimes I felt guilty, laying there, doing nothing but meditating and receiving loving energy. I was used to giving more than receiving. The belief, "It is better to give than to receive," was planted at an early age. I could see some of the societal conditioning rising as I surrendered to receive more love. Is *it really okay to lie around, do nothing and receive this much loving energy? It sure does feel good.*

At first I would rationalize to get rid of the guilt. *I don't have much choice. Besides, it is keeping me out of depression. What could be wrong with receiving love?* I was used to getting things done, being subtly and directly pushed by society through school and work; so doing nothing and receiving so much love was triggering. I could no longer push through things and get them done; my nervous system would flare up and my body would react with a "No." So I addressed the feelings of guilt. Interestingly enough, as I laid there doing nothing, nurturing the pain, addressing the guilt, I realized something was wrong with our society, not me.

> *Why isn't loving myself and listening to my inner rhythms okay? What's wrong with enjoying the simple things in life and enjoying more love and relaxation?*

By hanging out deeply in the inner rhythm of silence, we give ourself opportunities to address deep rooted conditioning. By facing conditioned beliefs and behaviors, we can shift and begin to receive more love, and in doing so, gain the capacity to give more love authentically.

I was becoming deeply connected to that inner 'something' that was moving me beyond conditioning and beyond the pain. That inner something, life force energy, was moving me, just at a slower pace and with more presence and love. The slower my actions became, the more I challenged the beliefs that I had to get things done, "be productive" and that accomplishing things meant I was worthy. As I surrendered to my inner rhythms and comforted the anxiety, I began accepting and trusting this slow *inner silence rhythm* as I listened moment to moment with presence to my body and intuitive mind.

> **My worthiness was shifting to "being" instead of "doing." This internal shift satisfied my heart and soul. Surrendering to my inner rhythms was pointing me to my true essence.**

The **slow rhythm** naturally came after resting in stillness and silence. Whether I was tired of lying down or had received enough soothing energy, that *something,* my life force energy, would move me again. I opened my eyes, stretched and rolled out of bed. Sometimes, I'd fall on the carpet still with some pain. I moved slowly while being present in my body. I took in my surroundings slowly until I felt connected in a gentle, loving way to my body and everything around me. This **slow rhythm** nurtured my mind and body.

> **Eventually, I'd get up. I was learning to trust
> and surrender to this *effortless flow* of
> my soul, which lies within my body.**

I could see that I was not moving life, but life was moving me. By listening to my own inner rhythm moment to moment, my core of self-love was getting stronger. I learned to be true to myself, to the rhythm that was in front of me and was right for me in the moment, even if others were going faster.

Then naturally, the energy would rev up and faster-paced movements would begin. I was surprised the **fast-paced rhythm** was still there; not for as long or as fast as it was before, but still alive in me. I would get up, move stuff around in my room and organize things for several minutes. I would go outside and experience the fresh air as I pulled a few weeds and swept the patio. *This feels so good,* I thought to myself, *movement.* After having my short-lived fill of movement, I'd come back inside. I learned to accept myself and love my rhythms as they were and for however long they lasted.

I'd open up my computer and write a little about my experiences or organize some more files. This was my **creative rhythm**. After several minutes of writing and organizing materials, I'd get up and dance and move about with a few exquisite moves and turns. Not like I used to do on the dance floor of course, but at least I thoroughly enjoyed a move or two before I laid down again.

After receiving more loving energy, I'd get up again
and bounce around while singing a song.
My *playful rhythm* was still there.

A little joy went a long way. I found myself moving toward my car. I grabbed the soft foods I had prepared from the kitchen, went outside and packed my car, getting ready for my part-time job as a nanny.

After all that, it was time for a pause. I sat in my car, feet up and head tilted back. These pauses were essential before and after movement and events. I relaxed into the car seat and called a friend to share what I was learning from this situation. I was ready for the ***rhythm of connection.*** We shared back and forth as we listened and allowed space for our experiences, feelings and emotions. After we hung up, a fearful thought arose. *How will I make it through this day and maintain my job?* I became exhausted so easily. I tried not to make myself wrong and instead reminded myself of how I am trusting and surrendering deeply to the moment.

I was surrendering to my inner rhythms and
the *effortless flow* of life and by doing so,
everything seemed to be working out.

There was chaos at times with my job as a nanny. During the **chaotic rhythm,** there was only so much I could handle. Any chaos and conflict was really hard on my nervous system, which had become incredibly sensitive. In a way, the increased sensitivity was a blessing. I practiced centering instead of paying attention to the chaos around me. As I drove my nanny-boy to his after school activities, I would listen to his day at school, hear honks and beeps from aggressive drivers, and quickly tap into my center and the loving source of energy that surrounded me.

These inner rhythms run through all of us individually and collectively. They run through our days, our months and every stage of our life. (Roth, 1998) By accepting these inner rhythms within ourselves, we become more accepting of the rhythms of others as well. The more we recognize, embrace and surrender to these rhythms, the more harmonious, alive and connected to our souls' journeys we become, even if there is pain.

EIGHT INNER RHYTHMS

1. INNER SILENCE

If we close the doors to the outer world, we can open to our inner reflections, observations and guidance. We can use this rhythm to integrate life's lessons. We all need silence to rest and reboot our energy systems. It may look as if there is nothing moving, yet inside, there is movement; all the rhythms exist inside. The minuscule movement of the particles and molecules in our bodies vibrate with the pulse of our hearts. The inner silence rhythm is one that allows us to sink into our Self. Often physical and emotional healing can occur. Images, sensations, thoughts and emotions rise and then settle in silence. The wonderful thing about silence is that it is always there, any time of the day or night; ready for us to pause and notice.

2. SLOW

In the slow rhythm of life, we become aware of details. We become mindful and intimate with the small things, that we do not normally notice when we are moving fast. This rhythm can appear sluggish, but in fact it is a way to slowly open and become deeply present with ourselves and our surroundings. We can notice the beating of our hearts, the sensations in our bodies and our breath. With deeper presence, we can notice flowers budding, birds chirping, insects moving and the artistry in homes. We can enjoy smells, sounds, colors, energy, words and bodily sensations, when we slow down. We take many pauses during the slow rhythm, as we give attention to life, and breathe and take in more love. During the slow rhythm, there is often a transition times as we emerge from inner silence in our morning meditation routines or slow down from chaos and the hustle bustle of everyday activities in the evening.

3. EFFORTLESS FLOW

The effortless flow rhythm is fluid, subtle, soft and flexible and runs through all the other rhythms, even chaos. When we relax into this flowing undercurrent, even challenges and obstacles can seem easy. Everything just falls apart, reorganizes and falls back into place. Events and people come together effortlessly, like a water current running through us. There is no trying or forcing anything to happen. The chattering mind takes a back seat and the intuitive mind, the wisdom of the body becomes the leader. We can surrender to this rhythm, keeping our focus on the effortlessness of life. Effortless flow moves through and around everything; that is why it is known as the mother of all the rhythms (Roth, 1998).

4.FAST-PACED

Fast, robust, yet grounded is this energetic rhythm. Sometimes it may look as if we are on a mission and cannot be bothered by anyone. This rhythm is direct and clear, precise and sometimes even fierce. Things get done: cleaning, building, fixing, running to the store, shopping and other focused tasks. The breath may quicken, as we are moving fast and at a steady pace. This rhythm often sprouts out of slow movement or the effortless flow. After this rhythm moves through, it is often time for inner silence or the creative rhythm. Sometimes however, fast-paced rhythms comes right before the storm of the chaos rhythm.

5. CREATIVE

When our muse comes out to play, so does our creative rhythm. We are full of ideas and inspiration. Playing music, writing, painting, gardening, singing, dancing, cooking, inventing and building are part of this rhythm. Perhaps there is a new invention unfolding. There is joy in creating. Being creative is not about forcing ideas or making them happen. If we try and make this rhythm happen, we can become frustrated and it feels like work. Sometimes ideas pop in effortlessly before the actual creation plays itself out. There is an element of timelessness in this rhythm as we experiment with form, sound and color and lose ourselves in the creative process. This rhythm often is sandwiched between effortless flow and the slow rhythm.

6. PLAYFUL

In the playful rhythm, we play. We become like children as we let ourselves be free. Being silly is fun. Being playful is expressed in all kinds of ways from playing games, making jokes or a funny face, having a good laugh, singing a simple song or dancing around with glee. Many of us have pushed the playful rhythm aside when we became "adults," focused on our careers and getting stuff done. We may feel vulnerable as we rediscover this rhythm and fully express our inner playfulness and joy because this rhythm was conditioned out of us. This rhythm often can come after chaos or after we have gone through some challenging times. The playful rhythm can rise at any moment, is spontaneous and makes us feel alive.

7. CONNECTION

As human beings, we all have the desire to connect at a heart level and to share common interests. We enjoy being seen and heard. We enjoy listening to and loving others. We do this through social conversations, touch and play. We have running and walking buddies, recreational pals, work connections, best friends, partners and family members. In the connection rhythm, we face our self and how it is to be in community. We choose people who support us and who we resonate physically, emotionally, mentally and spiritually. In this rhythm, we can practice healthy communication skills in order to stay connected to our self while in the company of others. When we have had our fill of this rhythm, we often desire silence and alone time to integrate the gifts and lessons we received from our human connections.

8. CHAOTIC

In the chaotic rhythm, it may feel as if everything is crumbling and falling apart. It can be an unexpected situation, opposing views, breakups, accidents, surgeries or disasters that come our way. The unknown is usually present. Incongruences and confusion can also be a part of this rhythm. Chaotic energy is uncontrollable and unmanageable. Although it can be held in a container of love, it can still be uncomfortable until the scattered energies land, transform and comes back into order. Surrendering is inevitable. Eventually, the chaos passes and we become grounded and clear on our next step. As we learn how to surrender and stay centered in our Self, without fighting or resisting, being in the chaotic rhythm of life becomes a lot easier. Sometimes a good walk, run or workout will be of benefit. Other times, we might need a good cry, time to our self, deep meditation or rest, to center and recharge. (Roth, 1998) Chaos often comes before the inner silence rhythm or the fast-paced rhythm as it works itself out.

When we get to know our inner rhythms, we get to know our true essence. We can notice the rhythms we feel uncomfortable experiencing and learn to accept them. In doing so, we accept our soul's journey. We can also heal conditioning from our society that tends to focus on and promote the fast-paced rhythm of productivity and doing more than the inner silence rhythm of being. In this way, we become more balanced and loving to our self and those around us.

These rhythms move through all of us. They move at different times and in different ways. We move slowly and fast. We move forward and backwards, up and down. Sometimes we stop and do nothing. We get confused, off balance, angry and frustrated. We laugh and play. We focus and create. We find ourselves alone and then with others. We speed up and run until our tank is empty. Then we surrender and do nothing again. That which flows through us and others, moment to moment is our individual life force energy that is connected to all the rhythms of life and to our hearts' and soul's desires.

INNER RHYTHMS AND AUTHENTIC MOVEMENT - PRACTICES

Do one practice a day.
If you enjoy it, circle the practice and
add it to your wellness tool box.

DAY 1 PRACTICE
Getting to Know Your Inner Rhythms

All eight rhythms exist within us. These rhythms move through everything (Roth, 1998). The rhythms can be explored, accepted and enjoyed when we learn to identify and understand them. This understanding creates more validation and awareness of our self, others and all of our unique journeys.

Inner Silence
Slow
Effortless Flow
Fast-Paced
Creative
Playful
Connection
Chaotic

1. *Throughout your day, ask yourself, "What rhythm am I experiencing right now?" See if you can identify the rhythm as you are experiencing it. Can you recognize all eight inner rhythms within yourself in one day?*

----

2. *Which rhythm feels most comfortable to you?*

3. *Which rhythm feels the least comfortable to you?*

Explore the discomfort in this rhythm. Challenge yourself to be with any fears or resistance during the day when this rhythm comes up. See if you can surrender to this rhythm more fully and allow it to be just as it is, knowing that it will pass.

4. *Which rhythm would you like to experience more of but haven't allowed yourself to enjoy?*

5. *What keeps you from experiencing and enjoying more of this rhythm?*

DAY 2 PRACTICE
Inner Silence and Slow Rhythm Practices

In this hectic, fast-paced world we live in, we rarely become present enough in our bodies to enjoy the inner silence and slow rhythm. This is because our society tends to emphasize the fast-paced rhythms of getting things done and being productive. Therefore, the importance of inner silence and the slow rhythm is rarely acknowledged.

There are many benefits to being silent, deeply present and moving slowly. We can experience more love and connection to our minds, emotions and bodies. Our nervous systems can deeply relax for greater healing as we let go of tension. We can become more peaceful, self-aware and mindful with our surroundings.

Take an hour or two, or whatever you have available, just for yourself. Make sure you have no plans or commitments during this time. This is a sacred time for you to be with your inner silence rhythm, and slow rhythm, a time to surrender and do absolutely nothing but be present with yourself.

1)Inner Silence Rhythm: Begin with inner silence; perhaps meditating, staring at nature, and/or observing your thoughts, emotions and sensations in your body. Do this in bed, lying on outside on the earth, in your favorite lounge chair or in your car. Notice your thoughts and mental activity, but do not let the busyness dictate what you will do next. Instead check in with your heart and your body. There is nothing for you to do but be present in the stillness of the current moment. (This can be a challenge sometimes, as anxiety and discomfort stored in our bodies can often arise when we slow way down.) Continue to lie there and be present with your breath, feeling every sensation in your body, and noticing every emotion, allowing them to just be and move through.

If you notice you are in your head, thinking you need to get things done, just stop and wait in the silence, until that urgent energy of doing passes. If it doesn't pass, affirm "It is safe for me to be in this moment and listen to my body and its inner rhythms." If anxiety arises, breathe through it and comfort your heart. (Most of us aren't use to making our inner rhythms a priority, so it's important to stay curious and gentle while exploring the emotions and sensations that come up.) Simply do nothing and wait for something to move you. This is a practice in and of itself. Let the inner rhythm of your body, the undercurrent of life move you slowly.

2)Slow Rhythm: *When your body wants to move, begin with the slow rhythm. Move one or two fingers very slowly. Notice how this slow, mindful movement affects your entire body. Pay attention to your breath as you move your hand very slowly. Be with the sensations in your body. Next, move one of your arms or legs slowly. Become aware of your breath as you make large, slow movements. Inhale, lifting your arms over your head and exhale, slowly bringing them down by your side. Move other parts of your body, as if in slow motion: foot, head, torso, etc. Do you notice physical sensations? ___ Do you feel more relaxed? ___ Are other emotions coming to surface?___*

Try lying on your back and roll side to side slowly. Then pause on each side for a few breaths. Bring both your knees into your chest. Experiment and do some of your own favorite stretches, only slow them way down.

     a. How did it feel to be in the silence for so long? What did you notice?

     b. How does it feel to slow down and move so consciously?

     c. What areas in your body are awakening as you do these movements?

    d. What benefits might you receive from doing these inner silence and slow rhythm practices more often?

DAY 3 PRACTICE
Chaotic Rhythm Practice

If you are feeling out of sorts, uncomfortable and in your head, overstimulated and overwhelmed, you are most likely in the chaotic rhythm. Sometimes, there is chaos going on in the world or around you and you may be picking it up. Or, you may be dealing with your own crisis, the unknown, a big change, or a situation/person that is out of control. Here's a practice that will help you get out of your head, let go of the tension and come back to balance. Find a place where you can move and make sound, your car, bedroom or backyard. Perhaps, go for a hike or drive in nature. Find a secluded place where you feel uninhibited and safe to express freely.

    1)*Time to shake it all loose and let it run through you so that you can come back to this present moment and feel centered again. Stand up (or sit/lie down) and begin to shake your body. Shake out every part of your body: your hands, arms, feet, legs, hips, torso, heart, neck and especially your head. Now do them all together at once. Release and let go. Keep shaking. Don't stop shaking until you feel you've had enough or are exhausted. When you are done, pause. Can you feel your breath? ___ Is your heart beating? ___*

    2)*Now go for a second round of shaking. Keep doing this practice until you've had enough. Maybe even a third round. Listen to your body, it will tell you when you are complete.*

    Are you present in this moment? How does your body feel?

This activity will get your heart beating and your mind will eventually let go. You can also add sound to this activity using a simple sound like "Ahhhh" or "Grrrr" (helps release anger and stuck emotions) as you move and shake.

This activity is twice as satisfying and fun, if you do it with a friend or a group of people.

Chapter 12

MUSIC, SINGING AND SOUND HEALING

"Music can be used not only to soothe us,
but also to stimulate us... It is a way to bypass the
'static' of purely rational thought patterns.
This may be the key to the mind body healing response."

NANCY KLEIN

IT WAS TIME TO ADDRESS TWO MORE MOLARS. THE PAIN IN THEM
was similar to the pain in the other three that had been pulled. *Why
not have them both pulled at the same time?* It would save me time,
money and pain. I knew the ropes. I talked to Dr. Geminiz about
my idea. He understood and agreed. *What a journey this has been.*
I felt grateful that I trusted myself and had an ally and friend in
Dr. Geminiz. He made the necessary phone calls and soon I had
an appointment for extracting two more achy molars. I was excited
about the possibility of someday waking up free of pain in my teeth.

The time had come. I sat in the surgical chair and tilted my head
back. I waited for Dr. Gregory, my main oral surgeon, to come in. I
was preparing my mind for the extractions. Because I was getting
two teeth pulled, Dr. Gregory suggested I have general anesthesia.
Normally, I would do local anesthesia and be able to walk out of
the operating room, but not this time. I took the day off work and
found someone to drive me there and back home. I faced the fear

Awaken Your Inner Physician

of not knowing what would be happening while I was knocked out. I was not going to be in control. This meant trusting the doctor and nurse completely. *Surrender, surrender,* became my mantra.

The time had come and I sat quietly in the surgical chair. I was grateful that the doctor's assistant granted me permission to play healing music during the surgeries. I put my music player off to the side on the counter, out of the way and turned it on. It was playing soft, relaxing music from some of my favorite artists.

By focusing on the relaxing current of sound, my body and breath let go of any stress and I began receiving healing energy.

A very close friend of mine was a DJ and he had gifted me several playlists of soft, peaceful music. I had shared with him my fear and anxiety while going through this situation, not knowing how it was all going to turn out and yet, taking the next, best step forward. He had selected healing songs just for me. Just feeling his love through the music gave me an extra feeling of support while I listened to the gentle, familiar songs while waiting for the surgeon.

The surgeon's assistant had left to get some things. Within a few minutes, she came back in the room. She offered me small white pillows to place under my head. I snuggled into the pillows while she sanitized the area. She had no idea how these small pillows nurtured me so. Anything gentle and soft was healing during these aggressive procedures. She then put some numbing gel around my teeth in preparation for the injections to come. *People of Love* by Snatam Kaur, one of my favorite songs and artist, began playing. As I listened to the positive lyrics and relaxing, soft music, I surrendered even more, "We are the people, people of love. Let us people love today..." Half way through the preparation, the assistant chimed in, "This music is really nice and relaxing."

"It calms my nerves," I added.

"It's calming for me too," she said, while continuing to prepare the room.

I felt relaxed and connected to her. I visualized my connection to my Higher Self and the doctor's Higher Self. *I can trust and let go, knowing we are connected,* I repeated to myself.

Listening to healing music before and during challenging situations can help us surrender and let go of fear and control. Music allows our bodies to relax so we can move through situations with greater ease. Healing sounds and words melt our worries and bring the separate parts of our body and mind back to wholeness.

Soon Dr. Gregory came in. "Hello Gerilyn," he said with a twinkle. He was positive, confident and upbeat. "Just a little pinch," he said. I was hoping this would be the last time I heard him say that. As he injected my gums, I focused on the music. Then he gave me a little pink pill. In minutes I was out. I woke up 45 minutes later and two molars had been extracted.

I was groggy. But I could hear the music still playing. I felt the comfort of the familiar, soothing music still playing. The doctor and assistant were in the room looking down at me. "The surgery went well," the doctor said and smiled at me.

The music in the background continued to anchor me back into the room and into the moment.

Dr. Gregory left and his assistant gave me some water and pain medication and told me I'd be able to rest in the room next door until my ride came. The music stopped right then. "Look at that, the music stopped just at we are finishing up," the assistant pointed out. I smiled with a half-numbed grin, amazed at the perfect timing. I was grateful that even though I wasn't conscious during the procedure, I felt connected to the doctor and nurse, knowing this healing music was playing through the entire surgery.

I was feeling woozy as she helped me out of the chair. "This way," she held my arm to steady me and escorted me to the room next door carrying my music player in her other hand. I laid down on a couch. There was water and a magazine on the table next to me. She placed my player on the floor near me.

When I arrived at home, I laid down and put on more soothing music. Emotions began to rise.

The music had a way of drawing out the deeper feelings associated with this difficult situation. I was in the safety of my own room where I could now express deep sadness. Tears flowed effortlessly and I felt a release of the bottled up energy I had been holding in my mind and body.

Music can often draw emotions out and does this in various ways. Healing music reminds us of our connection to the heart and to loving, life force energy.

Music can take us out of our analytical minds and into our hearts. Music can remind us of situations that we haven't yet dealt with or grieved. Songs can be metaphors for experiences that we have not been able to put into words on our own. Song lyrics can stir up past situations and provide us with an opportunity for deeper reflection. Deeper insights brought about by music can help us reclaim our power. Music can also stir up and help us express our greatest joy and happiness through singing and dancing.

On my way to work, I often listened to the top 40 pop stations. After such invasive procedures however, I needed gentle music to calm my nervous system.

The hustle bustle on the highway and added honks and beeps would rattle my nerves. I was very sensitive now and things that used to not be so disturbing became energetically amplified. I could feel when a pushy driver was behind me. In order to remain in an energetic, relaxed and healing mode, I would pop in the CD of the soothing sounds that my friend had created for me. This music would help me block out the unwanted sensory input of all the loud noises and aggressive energies around me (Tomatis, 2006). In this way, societal disturbances became secondary. I immediately centered in my body and relaxed.

**I felt comforted knowing, that at any time,
I could ground into my body and escape into
this nurturing music, no matter who was
around me or what was going on.**

Because we live in a society which is over stimulating with phones ringing, loud music playing, cars driving and honking, many voices talking at once and lots of other noise pollution, finding ways to center and balance ourselves is imperative. The everyday onslaught of aggressive energies and fast pace life styles can create an imbalance that affects our nervous system. The high energetic rhythm of excitement, productivity, pushing and racing through life creates unnatural tension in our body. Because our heart and body's rhythm are influenced involuntarily by the dissidence all around us, instead of slowing down, we automatically try to speed up to match the faster tempos. This constant discordant imbalance wreaks havoc and is stressful at a cellular level on our organs and to our psyche. it takes great effort to stay balanced and relaxed in this world. Healing music remind us of the effortless flow that is moving underneath all the chaos.

Natural tonal frequencies like ocean waves, water-falls and birds chirping remind us of the joy and effortlessness in our lives. Nature's rhythms help us connect to the deeper undercurrent of love. When we tune into nature, our heart rates slow down and our brainwaves become calmer. The harmonious essence and the sounds of nature help us attune to our inner essence and put us back into balance. Wooden instruments such as guitars, oboes, and drums help us remember our connection to our bodies and to the earth. Instruments like the flute, harp, piano, and violin remind us of a softer part of our self. Tibetan bowls and didgeridoos attune us to healing frequencies. The sounds of these instruments ground us and bring us back to our center.

Music with happy, joyful and positive lyrics can help with inner self-talk. We can get a "hit" of positive energy from the music and reprogram our minds with life-affirming words. Whether singing alone, with a friend or in a group, we receive positive vibrations which affect our minds, bodies and emotions. This feel-good energy extends out naturally into our community for greater healing.

**When driving my nanny-boy to water polo after school,
I would look for music on the radio that would
feel good energetically for both us.**

Most of the popular stations were strewn with songs of blame, attacking words and sexual fantasy.

The music was laden with lyrics of either romantic victims giving their power away or loud, fear-based aggressive, competitive phrases and images.

**I cared about his psyche and
well-being as well as my own.**

Being a pre-teen, he wanted to be cool and listen to some of the violent songs. I explained to him why I didn't like the songs and didn't want to fill his mind with violence and "junk food" music. Most importantly, however, I told him how much I cared about him. He agreed to only listen to songs that made us *both* feel good. He would occasionally test the waters and select songs that were chaotic and aggressive songs. Because I had established with him that I was the driver and had the first right to the radio stations and the songs we listened to, I used my veto power to make decisions that I felt benefited both of us energetically.

One time while driving to water polo practice, we were both rocking out to one of our favorite songs on the radio. His hands were in the air as his feet were stomping. My body was grooving as I sang along to a popular song. When we came to a stop sign, a car next to us saw us rocking out with joy. At first my nanny-boy was embarrassed and shrunk down in his seat so as not to be seen. The guy next to us began rocking out too, which I pointed out to my nanny-boy. He quickly sat up straight again, smiled and began putting his hands in the air again. So much joy. It's contagious!

All music is healing if it touches our soul and promotes positive emotions. Lyrical music induces play, joy and full expression. Music with a strong, steady beat can help us keep our momentum going while staying focused and getting stuff done. Deep, instrumental music can bring out our rich, tender emotions and move the deepest parts of our soul. Listening to music that is soft and sweet can remind us of nurturing, unconditional love, beckons healing energy and supports meditative practices. Even chaotic music has its purpose. It can be used to shake our bodies and minds clear from anything that no longer serves us. (Levitin, 2006)

At one of my appointments with my endodontist, Dr. Geminiz, I sat patiently waiting and sitting in the surgical chair so he could exam one of my teeth. There was office music playing. As Dr. Geminiz came in he started talking about the music that was playing, "Oh I love this one! Didn't it come out in 1980? It's an oldie but a goodie…" And then he started singing. "Whenever I see your smiling face, I want to smile right back because I love you…" I was laughing inside as his soulful voice filled the office with joy. He had no idea how his carefree, playful energy positively affected me as I sat in the chair.

**My endodontist's childlike spontaneous outburst of
song and not caring what anyone thought was
so refreshing in a time of hardship.
His voice wasn't necessarily of star quality,
but his energy was and lifted me up.**

There are many ways music, sound and song can be used as a healing modality. Whether through listening, humming, singing, chanting, movement or dance, we can open ourselves to fuller expressions of our self. Music can be used to help us get out of our chattering minds, to get into our bodies and to help us receive loving energy. We can use music and positive lyrics to remind us of the love that we are. We can use music to enhance our joy in our everyday activities. We can use music to help us slow down, meditate and integrate life's events. What a magical, mystical and joyful gift music can be!

MUSIC, SINGING AND SOUND HEALING - PRACTICES

Do one practice a day.
If you enjoy it, circle the practice and
add it to your wellness tool box.

DAY 1 PRACTICE
Healing Sound and Energy Awareness

Select some music that soothes and relaxes you. If possible, choose music without lyrics and that has a very slow, rhythmic beat or no beat at all. Sit or lie down and breathe deeply as you begin to slow your breath down. Inhale, as you count to three slowly and exhale, slowly counting to three. Allow your breath and the music to bring you into the present moment as your body relaxes. If your mind is busy with thoughts, let them pass by without attaching to them. If you do get lost in them, just gently bring your attention back to the music and your breath.

1. *Can you feel the music in your body?* ____

2. *Can you feel healing energy moving in your body while listening to the sounds of the music?* ____

You may begin to notice sensations in and around your body. Perhaps, you may feel some tingling, a chill, some heat, expansiveness or maybe you notice some tightness in your body. As you keep bringing your attention inward, allow the music and breath to take you into a deeper and even more relaxed state. Continue returning your attention to your body and remain open to receiving healing energy while listening to the music for as long as you enjoy.

DAY 2 PRACTICE
Sounding as a Way to Release and Heal

Find a space where there is little to no distraction and where you feel comfortable making sound without feeling inhibited.

Begin by making an audible sigh. Take a long, deep, slow breath in and then exhale as you say and sound "Ahhhhh." Let it last the entire length of your exhale. This toning sound will relax your mouth and open your airways. (It is important not to force the sound out, but make it as natural as your breath.) Repeat "Ahhhh" a few times. Notice the particular note you are sounding.

Can you feel the vibration in your body as you sound/tone? ____

Where in the body do you feel it? ____

Now, intentionally play with different tones; high, middle and low tones as you sound and say "Ahhhh."

1. *Where do you feel the higher tone vibrating in your body?*

   _____

   _____

2. *Where do you feel a middle tone in your body?*

   _____

   _____

3. *Where do you feel the lower tone in your body?*

   _____

   _____

Perhaps while you are sounding, there is some suppressed emotion that is wanting to come through. There may be some unexpressed anger or other emotion your body has stored that wants to come out. Don't hold back as you inhale and exhale "Ahhhh." Give yourself the freedom to sound as loudly as you want with as much emotion as you want. Inhale again and sound with even greater intensity. Let the sound be bold and clear as you exhale. Now is the time to allow any stuck emotions to move through the body's tissues with the use of sound. Do this several more times. After you are complete, notice your breath and notice how your body feels.

4. *Where in your body do you feel more open?*

_____

_____

5. *How do you feel emotionally as a result of this practice?*

_____

_____

6. *What sensations do you notice in your body? How would you describe your body energetically?*

_____

_____

_____

_____

Thank yourself for the release and opening.

DAY 3 PRACTICE
Enhance-Your-Inner-Rhythms Music

In the previous chapter, you were given the eight rhythms that your body experiences on a daily basis. If you haven't done the practices in the previous chapter on the eight rhythms, it might be a good idea to review and engage in it before trying this practice. There are many types and styles of music that mirror your inner rhythms.

Here are some "Inner Rhythms" music ideas that can help enhance your day as experience the rhythms. See if you can identify the different kinds of music you enjoy with the various rhythms you go through in your day. Perhaps some artists, genres and musical styles are in your own music collection.

1. ***Inner Silence Music:*** *If you desire silence, so that you can relax your mind, integrate your day and come back to center, find music that is soft, slow, melodic and has no words. What kinds of music comes to mind for the inner silence rhythm?*

   _____

   _____

2. ***Slow Rhythm Music:*** *If you are wanting to move slowly, with a relaxed focus, perhaps stretching, laying on the earth, doing Tai Chi or Gentle Yoga, find music that has a very, slow steady beat, a few words and is relaxing for your nervous system. What kinds of music would you listen to for the slow rhythm?*

   _____

   _____

3. ***Effortless Flow Music:*** *If you are in the flow, moving about from here to there, enjoying your surroundings and in your body, find music or sing a song that is up-lifting with a steady, happy beat. What music might you sing or listen to as you enjoy the effortless flow rhythm?*

   _____

   _____

4. **Fast-Paced Rhythm Music:** *If you are in the mode of getting stuff done and moving at a fast pace, find music that has a quick tempo and fast beat to enhance this inner rhythm. What type of music might you listen to for the fast-paced rhythm?*

_____

_____

5. **Creative Rhythm Music:** *If you are working on a creative project, listen to music that helps bring out your muse and helps your mind focus is important. What kind of music do you think would help your creativity come out and help your mind focus while going through the creative rhythm?*

_____

_____

6. **Playful Music:** *If you are wanting be silly, and feel moved to express yourself in a fun, playful way, find music that brings you joy and is upbeat. What music brings you some bounce in your steps and great happiness and represents the playful rhythm?*

_____

_____

7. **Connection Music:** *To connect with others, you can use any type of music that both you and your friend/ partner enjoy. Who do you enjoy listening to music or dancing with and what type of music would enhance the relationship? What music comes to mind for the connection rhythm?*

_____

_____

8. *Chaotic Music:* If you have just had an interaction or a day filled with challenges, confusion and chaos, and you have a lot of energy running through you that you'd like to release, listening to music that is very, very fast, maybe even dissonant will help you shake loose all the energies around you. What artist or type of music might you listen to during the chaotic rhythm?

Chapter 13

PRESENT TOUCH
AND MASSAGE

*"Present touch is not measured by how many times
you touch each other but by how many
times you reach each other."*

CATHY MORANCY

BECAUSE OF ALL THE ORAL SURGERIES AND DOCTORS' VISITS, MY
jaw and neck were unusually tight. The anxiety of having so many
people probing inside my mouth with their hands, injecting needles, pulling teeth and poking into my gums, took its toll on my
body and my nervous system. The base of my neck and the joints
in my jaw were tight from all the stress and tension. My temples,
jaw, neck, heart and other areas of my body needed loving presence so they could heal and integrate all that had taken place.
Every morning, I was present with myself. I listened to my body
and the areas that spoke the loudest; that which had the most
intense sensations and pain.

This morning the intensity was in my neck. As best as I could, I
put my fingers into the tightest spots along the base of my neck and
then along each side of my neck, along my spine, where my muscles
were extremely tight. I used my fingers, hands and sometimes my
knuckles. I would sense the amount of pressure; first light touch
and then deeper into the tissues as they relaxed and opened.

I was a Certified Massage Therapist (CMT) and Reiki Master Teacher (RMT) and had given many of my clients deep tissue massage. With them I created a loving space as I helped them relax and open their bodies for greater healing, emotionally, mentally and spiritually. Now it was my turn.

Initially, my thoughts would bounce all over the place. By having my hands on my body though, I was able to focus on the sensations in my body instead of the thoughts. I focused on my breath and the place of contact that was receiving loving presence. After several minutes of presence, my thoughts began to settle. My body began to follow suit and relaxed, receiving loving energy and surrendering more deeply.

As I nurtured and dug deep into my neck and jaw line, suppressed anxiety and fear came up. In my room, I felt safe enough to validate the emotions that were coming up, first fear and then anxiety. Then with greater loving presence, I sensed some sadness. No tears came, just a sensing. Compassionate thoughts came up too. *You made it through. Time for healing.* Then more sweet, healing energy arose. It softened me enough that I could go into some tight and knotted up places that were located in the base of my neck. After several more minutes, I readjusted my hands and dug deeper in the occipital ridge and placed a hand on my heart. A steady current of healing energy gushed through. More emotion rose up. *It is safe to feel.* Tears came and rolled down my cheeks. The tightness in my neck, jaw and temples began to soften even more. *Ahhhhhhh.* More grief and sadness released at a cellular level.

**Stresses and memories from the past lodge
themselves in the tissues of the body.
When we give ourselves deep loving presence
in a safe place, we allow for deeper
healing and love to come in.**

Sometimes my hands would get tired so I would grab a rock and lay it under the back of my head and neck to give my hands a break. By pinpointing the spots that were tender or aching, I could give myself a passive massage and acupressure treatment. In this way, the acupressure was similar to an acupuncture treatment, only I used rocks instead of needles. After the back of my head and neck relaxed, I often shifted the rocks and placed the sharper edge to gently dig into areas alongside my spine, one rock on each side starting on the upper back and moving down to the lower back. The energy became a strong river flow throughout my entire body.

Because I was in a safe place, I was able to give myself as much time and focus as I needed and wanted. After a while, I drifted into an even deeper relaxed state. The tension was melting away in areas that I hadn't noticed before. My entire body was receiving a light bath and letting go of trauma from surgeries gone by. I watched the held tension of defensiveness in my body transform to expansiveness. I could feel the subtle cellular structure reorganizing around my teeth where the extractions were done. Deep healing was taking place.

> **Being present in our bodies, using touch**
> **and massage has many benefits.**
> **We become aware of our bodies, minds and**
> **emotions and get to know them intimately.**

We become empowered as we learn how to become present with our bodies and become open to healing at deeper levels. We become familiar with where we hold stress, past injuries and trauma and learn to break up old scar tissue, both emotionally and physically. Present touch helps us get out of our intellectual mind and connect with our innate loving, healing energy. We learn to trust ourselves and our intuition as we strengthen our inner listening skills. Through touch and massage our muscles and tissues relax so we can be both strong and flexible.

Present touch and massage increases circulation of blood and lymph. It can alleviate pain in the back, neck, shoulders, feet and hands. It can help with arthritis, asthma, bladder weakness, carpal tunnel, lung infections, colds, sinuses, constipation, mild depression, earaches, appetite control, eyestrain, hypertension, irritable-bowel syndrome, menstrual cramps, migraines, sore throats, sprains, ulcers, stress relief and much, much more. (Mally, 1998, Jones, 2009) Giving and receiving present touch with *others* has many healing benefits as well.

> **Present touch fulfills the human need**
> **for connection. It is safe intimacy**
> **with the purest intent.**

Unfortunately, touch has been confused with romantic interest that usually comes with an agenda and ulterior motives. When touch has a hidden agenda of getting sex as the main motivation, anger, fear and confusion can set in. That is because this type of touch tries to take energy from another person and is draining. From this place, touch does not have a pure intent. Unfortunately, media promotes aggressive, dominating and sexually motivated touch. This leads to more disconnections between men and women and distrust of touch (Smith, 2009). Present touch is amazingly healing for those who have a history of receiving unloving, forceful touch with selfish agendas.

Present touch is *always* healing. It is more than a quick back rub, a hug or exerting effort to get muscles to let go by rubbing and rubbing. Present touch comes from the heart with a deep presence and energetic, healing intent. This kind of touch comes through the heart and hands/body and it wants nothing in return. No force, no wanting, or trying to make something happen is involved. Instead, present touch is given by centering into the body and surrendering to the universal life force energy that flows through you and through the person with whom you are in contact. Present touch feels good and s mutually satisfying. It is beneficial for all ages, babies, children and adults.

**Of course, everyone has different degrees
of comfort regarding touch and it is
important to respect that.**

For some, touching their back may be too much, but having their hand held is fine. It is wise and respectful to ask someone before you touch them. Unless, of course, you know them well and have established a sincere connection; then permission may not be necessary. Using your intuition and asking others questions such as, "How does this feel? Would you like the touch to be softer or deeper? Let me know when you have had enough, okay?" will help you determine how much touch others enjoy and create a safe atmosphere.

Present touch and play can bring about a life-time of connection and enjoyment. There are so many ways to bring touch and connection into our daily lives with our self, a significant other, friends, family and community. Here are a few healthy touch options.

DAILY HEALTHY TOUCH ACTIVITIES

1. Simply touching someone with presence, on the hand, shoulder or back.

2. Holding hands with a beloved or walking arm and arm with a friend.

3. Back scratches or arm scratches. (With nails is the best!)

4. Foot and hand massages. (Go to the library and check out a reflexology book for added interest.)

5. Scalp massages and gentle hair tugging.

6. Playful wrestling for connection and fun. (Not for competition or domination.)

7. Experimental touching games. (Tapping, patting, rolling and sliding with touch.)

8. Trade massages with someone for fun. (Try using different parts of your body, like your forearms, elbows or feet.)

9. Self-massage. (Use tennis balls or rocks and place them under the areas that are tight. Surrender into them and focus on your breath.)

10. Partner present touch while meditating. (Place your hands/body on an area of the receiver and focus on the breath and healing energy with very little movement if any. Move hands as guided.)

11. Family yoga and playtime. (Parents pose in a yoga position and kid's balance on them.)

12. Contact improvisation (Contact Improv. Begin by sitting back to back with someone and move slowly side to side and up and down. Take a class or get a DVD. Van, 2016)

13. Hire a massage therapist for an evening. (Learn different strokes, pressure points and energy awareness with a friend or your partner. Williams, 2009, Clay & Pounds, 2003)

Present touch is for everyone, young and old. It helps us stay relaxed, flexible, connected and aware of our bodies. It helps us bring loving energy to our muscles, tendons, fascia, skin, heart, lungs, spleen, reproductive organs and nervous system. In this way, we help prevent illness, ward off diseases and learn healthy methods of maintaining physical, emotional and mental well-being.

PRESENT TOUCH AND MASSAGE - PRACTICES

Do one practice a day.
If you enjoy it, circle the practice and
add it to your wellness tool box.

DAY 1 PRACTICE
Loving, Present Touch with Self

One thing is for certain; present touch is always available. Most people don't think about giving themselves presence using touch and their own hands, unless it's of a sexual nature. However, present touch is one of the greatest gifts you can give yourself every day. Touch is good for your nervous system, muscles, tendons, ligaments, fascia and is especially healing for the heart.

Begin with resting both hands gently on your heart. Stay there for a while and see if you are able to feel the love and compassion for yourself. See if you can make a distinction between YOU and your body as the love flows through your hands.

Now place your hands behind your head or on your forehead. Try to relax and send love through your heart to your brain. Your brain is always working so hard and rarely gets the love it deserves. Now place your hands on your solar plexus, rib cage area. Take a few slow, deep breaths. Notice if you are holding any tension in those areas and be willing to let it go.

Move your hands to the belly and stomach area. Send love through your hands and with your thoughts. Take a few more mindful breaths and bring awareness to your body. Allow yourself to relax even deeper as you receive loving life force energy. Now, rest your hands on other parts of your body that you sense would benefit from loving attention: the brow, shoulders, hips, legs, etc.

Next, find an area in the body that is a bit tight and perhaps wants some deeper physical presence and exploration. Take your thumb and/or fingers and press firmly around the tightened area. Work from the outside edges and move toward the center, where most of the tightness lies. As you move closer into the tightest areas, it is normal for them to be a little tender. Bring yourself to the edge, to where if you applied any more pressure, it would not feel good, and yet it feels good with the amount of pressure you are giving. Stay on this edge and "hang out" with the intention of giving deep presence and loving energy into the muscles, tendons and bones. See what arises as you give presence. Notice how your tissues respond to the pressure and touch.

1. *Check in with the area of tightness in your body where you have given loving presence. Have you had enough touch? How do you know when you have had enough pressure? Do you want to dig in a little deeper?*

   _____

   _____

2. *Is there another tense part of your body that is desiring to be touched with deeper pressure?*

   _____

   _____

   If yes, then move your hands accordingly. With each breath allow your heart to connect to where your hands land. Continue to breathe deeply as you go into the tight areas, finding the edges of pain where it feels good. Stop when you feel complete.

Added Tips for Pressure Point Self-Massage with Objects: Try using various objects to apply pressure to tight areas in the body.

You may want to play with tennis balls for soft tissue pressure points, and rocks for deep tissue pressure points. Experiment with the various sizes of rocks for the back of your head (occipital ridge), along your spine (erector spinae), buttocks, thighs, hamstrings, ankles, arms, etc. The intention is to use gravity and the weight of your body as you lay on the rocks to bring presence to those areas. You can adjust the rocks to lie under various muscles as you receive healing presence and energy in the area you place them. Using rocks and tennis balls can lead to profound relaxation and meditational states. Add some soft healing music and go even deeper with this practice.

When you are done with your healing touch session, gently sweep or pat the areas in your body that you have given presence. Perhaps close the session by giving your body and mind a loving affirmation, "Thank you for giving me loving attention and healing presence," and then move onto the rest of your day!

DAY 2 PRACTICE
Loving, Present Touch with Others

Have you ever been touched or massaged by a person who was not fully present with you or had ulterior and/or sexual motives? _____ If so, you probably notice the experience was not relaxing or enjoyable. That's because a person with an agenda who is in their head and wanting something from you, cannot be present and in the moment with you. Having any kind of agenda with touch is the furthest thing from being present there is and is NOT present touch.

Present touch is about being in the heart, with the purest intent of channeling love and well-being through the hands. When we are in the present moment and are sending loving energy to another, it almost always feels good.

It is also very important to get consent before touching someone, unless of course you have already established a "free to touch" agreement, meaning you have touch already incorporated into your friendship/relationship.

Find someone who is interested in exchanging present touch. You may want to set a timer, say 15 or 30 minutes each. The job of the person who is giving touch is to be fully present. This means there is a deep listening to one's intuition and the requests of the receiver.

1. *Together, decide how long each of you will be giving/receiving touch.*

2. *Decide who will give touch first.*

3. *Then, make an agreement that if you are the receiver, you will speak up when you are desiring a certain type of touch: i.e., light, medium, deep, just presence and loving energy, pressure point massage, etc. Also, agree that you will speak up in the moment, if you want to be touched differently or on another part of the body.*

4. *Lastly, check to see if there are any parts of the body that the receiver does NOT want touched: i.e., an injury, a bruise or sensitive area.*

Before you begin, make sure the receiver is in a comfortable position, sitting or lying down. Ask the receiver if there is anything you can do to make them feel more comfortable.

Center yourself, take a few breaths and come into the present moment. You may want to say a loving intention for yourself and the receiver, out loud or to yourself. Example: "May I be a conduit of love

for _____ *(their name) highest good."*
Then put your hands together and warm them up with the intention of
connecting to universal love energy through your heart and your hands.

Gently place your hands on the receiver's shoulders or forehead.
Be still as you feel the connection between your heart and theirs.
Imagine loving energy coming through your hands.

After you've established the touch connection, you might want
to ask the following questions at various times during the massage.

1)"How does this pressure feel?"

2)"Would you like the touch to be deeper or lighter?"

3)"Would you like me to do anything differently?"

Now move from the forehead and shoulders, to the right or left
arm. Pause occasionally, remembering the healing energy moving
through your heart and hands. Move your hands slowly, with pres-
ence, down each arm. You may want to pause and massage deeper
and dig in with your thumbs and fingers as your intuition guides
you. Then make your way down their back, pausing with presence
and massaging as guided. Move to the sides of their hips, legs, calves,
ankles and feet. Again, remember to pause and give presence with
loving energy. (Because the belly is a more vulnerable area, you may
want to ask if it is okay to place your hands there. If you are guided to
have movement in your hands, do so very slowly and with presence.)

While massaging, imagine healing energy going to different
organs: the heart, lungs, spleen, kidneys, intestinal tracts and stom-
ach. Listen to your intuition as it guides you. Stay out of your head
and just feel which way your hands want to go and how deep. You
can always ask the receiver how your touch feels or if they want it
deeper or softer, to be reassured.

Note: As the giver, sometimes your mind may start to analyze
and chatter. Take a few breaths and ground into the earth, staying
present without talking. Eventually, the thoughts will pass and you
will be present again with their body and yours.

After both of you have received a massage, you may want to
share your experiences.

DAY 3 PRACTICE
Loving, Touch - Body Inventory and Mirror Work

Loving, Touch - Body Inventory: All of us have inherited images and beliefs from society that make our bodies wrong for being the way they are: too big, too small, too skinny, too short, too tall, too flat, too frail, too saggy, too wrinkly and so on. Society's body labels of "perfection" have influenced us all. Loving our bodies as they are and having unconditional, self-love for our unique body types and individual journeys is paramount for happiness and well-being.

1. *Sense into your body and ask yourself; which parts of my body have I indirectly or directly judged to be not good enough or compared unfavorably to others?*

   _____

   _____

   For women, we are most often self-conscious about the stomach, thighs, butt and breasts. For men, it is often the areas of the abdomen, arms and legs.

2. *Place your hands with loving awareness on those parts of your body you have judged and give them as much self-love as you possibly can.*

3. *Along with present touch, add some loving affirmations while giving presence to those neglected and ignored parts of your body.*

   "I am willing to accept _____ _____ (name the body part your hands are on) just as you are. You have served me well by _____

   _____ (name actions or pleasure). You are loved and

deserve to be loved."

Give that area as much healing energy as the body part is able to receive.

Mirror Work: You can take this activity a little further and do some work while looking in a mirror. Using a mirror can be a very powerful healing instrument. It is important to be very gentle while doing this activity as it may stir up a lot of emotions.

Find a mirror that displays your entire body. Look at yourself. See what thoughts rise up in your mind as you scan your body.

Say some affirmations and see how your heart responds. "My body is perfect as is. My body has served me well. My body is beautiful with all my unique soul's experiences and attributes. All areas deserve to be loved without exception."

Then go to the areas that you or someone else may have neglected or judged as too big, too skinny, too flat, too bumpy, too saggy, etc. Lovingly, lay your hands on those areas while you look at yourself in the mirror.

State the loving affirmations again. "My body is perfect as is. My body has served me well. My body is beautiful and holds all my unique soul's experiences and attributes. All areas deserve to be loved."

In the silence, see what emotions arise. If tears come, remember tears are a gift for healing the heart. Accept them graciously.

Make it a practice to give these neglected areas on your body present touch and loving affirmations of acceptance every day. Or you can set a special day aside once or twice a week to love your body just the way it is through touch or mirror work.

Chapter 14

A SOUL'S AWAKENING WITH LIFE LESSONS OF LOVE

*"Every relationship, every situation is part
of a divinely created and highly specific
curriculum for your soul's growth."*

MARRIANE WILLIAMSON

WHAT BEGAN AS A SEEMINGLY AVERAGE, MIDDLE AGE RECONSTRUC-
tion of some faulty teeth, ended up turning into a two-and-a-half-
year journey of chronic pain, anxiety and living in the unknown.
First some pain, then a couple of root canals, crowns, then a tooth
had to be pulled. I had seen 17 specialists, including a dentist, an
orthodontist, an endodontist, x-ray specialists, three prosthodon-
tists, three oral surgeons, two chiropractors, an internal medicine
doctor, two jaw specialists, an acupuncturist and two massage
therapists. In the end, seven teeth had been pulled. At last, the
physical pain in my teeth was gone. My nervous system however,
was shot and my neck and jaw were tight, and I still had no bite.

It was time to find a new prosthodontist. I looked on-line for
one near me. The list was fairly short and "Dr. Nelson," was a definite *No* - too pushy and he didn't make time for my questions. As I
perused the names that were left, I listened carefully to my intuition.
*Which one is saying yes? Which one pops out the most and gives my
body an expansive feeling? This one?* I listened carefully and received

a *Maybe. This one? No. How about this one?* I felt an expansion in my body. *Yes.* I looked over the names a few more times to see if any others were a *yes.* There was only one that stood out. "Dr. Patricia Halvi." This two-and-half-year journey had strengthened my intuition. I had learned how to ask questions and to listen and trust the kinesthetic response in my body.

With anticipation, the next week I drove to Dr. Halvi's office for an initial consultation. After parking in the rear, I walked around to the front and was welcomed with a painted, pink and green rose on the front door of her office. *A good sign, the symbol of love.* I definitely needed some tenderness after all I had been through. I filled out paperwork, took x-rays and was ushered into the adjacent room where Dr. Halvi was sitting behind a narrow desk.

"Hello, Gerilyn," she said as she pointed to the chair on the other side of the desk. "How are you doing? I see you have been through quite a bit." Her voice was soft and pleasant. As I sat down, I told her my story and how I hadn't had a proper bite for two and a half years and had been juicing and eating soft foods. I had lost nearly 30 pounds.

Dr. Halvi showed me my x-rays and gave me an explanation regarding my teeth and why so many of the back molars needed to be extracted. She explained, "You have an overbite. And because of your bite, you have put constant pressure on your back molars. And after 50 years of use, they fractured and cracked." Her words were validating, so simple and yet, clear. It took this long to have a doctor put it all together. Her culminating words spoken so sweetly put my body at ease. I felt as if I could settle in, as if I had finally come home from a long trip of the unknown.

Over the next several months, I had many visits with Dr. Halvi. She made a couple different molds of my teeth. Her intent was to create an upper partial denture that would give me a proper occlusion with my remaining teeth and my implant. I was hopeful. She made my incisors touch for the first time so that my bite would not only be dependent on the back molars. I was grateful that Dr.

Halvi had come up with a plan and laid out a financial payment plan that worked for my budget also.

The big day finally came! I sat eagerly awaiting my new partial as Dr. Halvi brought my denture in. Emotions sprang up. I sat with tears running down my face; happy, yet grieving all that I had lost and gone through. She handed me a few tissues. "You've gone through a lot." There was compassion in her face and it came through her hands as she held the partial and placed it gently in my mouth. "How does that feel?" A smile came over my face as I wiped the tears away.

"Thank you so much!" The final step in this long process was completed.

"Now you can eat all the foods you enjoy," she said and handed me a container for my partial. "The partial may take a while to settle in. You may need a few more adjustments. That's normal." She showed me how to clean it and we hugged as I said "thank you" again and expressed my sincere gratitude. I went to the front desk and paid my last payment. I shared my happy news with the receptionist whom I had gotten to know quite well. We celebrated with a high five. Driving home, I was overjoyed feeling the completion of a very long, arduous process with so many lessons along the way.

That night I laid in bed and
reflected back on my journey.

I didn't get braces. I didn't have orthognathic (jaw) surgery as one dentist thought I needed. I didn't have 16 of my teeth crowned to create proper occlusion as another prosthodontist specialist suggested. I didn't need to be on medication for the rest of my life as another oral surgeon said I needed to do. I am no longer dealing with chronic pain every day in my mouth. I wasn't financially wiped out either. (It did cost a lot, though.) I didn't lose my job. I didn't go on disability (which I thought was a possibility).

After a week or two, I noticed my strength was coming back. Pain takes a lot of energy to sit with and nurture. I have been like a child, eating whatever I want since I regained the ability to chew properly! I bought crackers, popcorn, pizza, chips, sushi, nuts, and croutons for a salad. I over did it a bit and my jaw started aching again. I took that as a sign that I still needed to be gentle.

Everything didn't end up picture perfect. Because of the stresses of so many invasive and aggressive surgeries, I still have some aches and pains that weren't there before, especially in my neck. There is still anxiety that is releasing at a cellular level. Having teeth pulled is not easy on the body or nervous system. I have some PTSD from all the aggressive and invasive procedures that I am embracing. The good thing is that I have all the tools and practices I need in order to be with the emotions, sensations and stresses in my body when those things do arise.

**I learned a lot over the past few years.
I learned to listen deeply to my body and
my inner wisdom before all else.**

I realized doctors and dentists are not perfect. The pedestal I once put them on no longer exists. They are human and they make mistakes. They are souls, just like me, who are learning their own lessons.

Doctors do know a lot and while I do respect their knowledge, they don't know everything nor do they know my body and what it needs as well as I do. I learned to listen to and trust that inner wisdom beyond the doctors' knowledge. The mistakes that were made along the way were mostly minor with a couple of bigger ones thrown in the mix too. I learned to have compassion for the doctors, but also to trust my Inner Physician and speak up when I knew I didn't need more medication, x-rays or root canals.

The lessons of self-love ran extremely deep.

For the first time, I had to make myself my number one priority. I had to do this not just some of the time, or most of the time, but *all* of the time. The pain was so great that I had no choice. This gave me the opportunity to look at the co-dependent conditioning I had at a subtle level and how at times, I made other's needs a priority at the expense of my own.

The pain prompted me to check in to my core almost every other moment asking, *what would give me the greatest comfort and love right now?* Often it was just lying and placing my hands on the area that was aching. I didn't have the energy to do much else during these years of constant pain and doctors' appointments. It was simple things that gave me the greatest enjoyment: taking a shower, cooking, a little gardening and connecting with close friends. I enjoy slowing down now and being more present and connected with love for the simple things in life.

Even though the pain is not there like it was,
I still ask myself;
what will expand me or give me the
greatest joy in this moment?

Now I don't care as much what others think of me; I'm not so dependent on love from outside sources. I know love dwells within and I can tap into it at any time. I take more time for me. Every morning I begin with deep, inner self love through meditation, laying still and embracing all aspects of myself. I follow that with self-massage and presence to my body. As I slowly get up, I connect with nature, drink water and eat from its bounty. Love doesn't cost anything and is so satisfying. It's as simple as presence with my body, food, flowers, the sun and deep friendships. I engage in creative projects when I feel like it, not because I have to, but because it gives me pleasure. Deep richness now lies in the love and presence of life.

My focus has changed from doing to being. With the foundation of being as my focus, my doing then comes not from feeling obliged or pressured, but from a place of peace, joy and presence.

My inner listening reflexes are stronger now. I am much quicker at saying "yes, no" or "not sure, will let you know." That's because I listen to my subtle body cues, my inner "yeses" which are expansive and "nos" which are contracted. I walk away from situations much faster if they are the least bit draining. I'm not so wishy-washy anymore. The guilt of being "selfish" still rises at times, but I see through it. I know I'm not being selfish from the ego's point of view; I'm being true to my Higher Self. I'm Higher Selfish. I have come to know that my peace, relaxation, expansion and joy are gifts to others as they give others permission to find the same.

Another lesson I learned was the acceptance of death, dying and the impermanence of life.

I laid in bed often, thinking of the impermanence of my teeth and body. *Things break down. It's part of the aging process.* My back molars did. I had never really thought about or faced death and dying to this degree or quite so personally before this situation. Letting go and releasing is an important skill in life. I learned to acknowledge and embrace my aging process and death itself while staying connected to the life force that still moves through me.

I remember looking at my garden and seeing the last of the tomatoes hanging. Harvest season in my garden was over. The tomato plant was starting to yellow and shrivel. I realized nature's way of living and dying was mirroring my own body. *My body is decomposing naturally.* I thought about my body again. *Nothing is solid. Nothing is permanent. This body, these teeth are not solid.* Then deeper reflections around impermanence came. *If everything is impermanent, if everything is always changing and shifting, then there is nothing I can totally depend on.* I sat with this for a while. Then I asked myself a deeply, self-reflecting question.

> **If my security does not lie in my body, this situation, or**
> **with the doctors, or any person, then where**
> **does my security lie?**
> **I waited for an answer.**
> **This is what came.**
> *My security lies in the ever-expanding universe,*
> *which is changing moment to moment.*

This vast eternal love is what I surrendered to, like never before. The pain was the impetus again and again to remind me to surrender and be present in the moment. The pain supported me in dropping down out of my head and into my body. I would lay awake and nurture the pain in the morning, in middle of the day, in the evening and even in the middle of the night. Along with the nurturing of pain, I was doing deep, inner healing work. Sometimes this inner work was easier to do in the middle of the night when the analytical, monkey mind was not so active. The more I experienced living in the moment and being present in my body, the more I could see that the analytical mind and all its mental activity was not in control. There was a life force energy in my body, in my heart and soul that was moving me.

> **I learned to surrender to this life force energy,**
> **dropping from the analytical mind into the**
> **undercurrent of my soul and body again and again.**

I learned to ignore the mind's chatter. I learned to distinguish the difference between the busy, dithering mind and that small still voice that has few words and the intuitive body that knows. Being so present and attentive to myself, I could see that everything I needed to say or do was available right in the very moment that existed. I could now see clearly, the magic and effortless flow of life. My needs were always met and lessons of love were constantly being offered and learned.

I wondered, *maybe the clock, time as I know it, isn't running the show; maybe this life force energy is?*

Even the time clock as I knew it became secondary to surrendering to my soul's life force and the present moment. I noticed I was always on time when following my inner guidance. I often had experiences of magically running into the people I needed to see and was amazed at how effortlessly situations worked themselves out. Of course, I watched my fearful conditioning telling me that I would be late or get in trouble, but could see that that was only my mind at work and I practiced ignoring its fearful chatter.

I had many mornings that I was just too exhausted to get up. Pain is tiresome. Sometimes I would challenge the universe; *I'm not getting up until I feel good* and I didn't care what happened. It was as if I was going through an initiation of sorts. *I'm willing to let go of everything, my finances, my job, my friends, my family and even my daughter.* I still loved them, I just had to let go because of the pain. I was unable to give to others or do much of anything but take care of myself. I was not in control. It was a time for deep surrendering and remembering what is really true. I began noticing that this same energy that was moving me to get up or lay down, was moving everyone else too. This meant facing my fears and judgments about myself and others and letting them go.

I was completely surrendered, experiencing a true emptiness. As I sat with the pain, exhausted, not knowing my next step, I'd surrender to this loving energy that was running through my body. It was beyond my thoughts and my monkey mind, beyond the pain and confusion. Then after being recharged, seemingly out of nowhere, something would eventually get me up and get me moving. This happened again and again throughout the three years of chronic pain. *What was this something?* I asked. The answer I received was this.

Love is moving me and it is moving us all.

Then I experience a couple of days when my ego was completely gone. There was no wanting anything to be different than it was. I had experienced moments of this before when my thoughts had taken a backseat. But not for two days! During this time, I was present with only the life force energy that was moving me. I was neutral; I had no judgments of anything or any situation. I was seeing life from a different perspective. This perspective was from a higher place, from my Higher Self or awareness. Only soul lessons and love were present. There was no hierarchy in this realm.

**Everyone was just a human being experiencing
and having their own unique soul's lessons as
though they were written into the script of life.
This was one of my greatest awakenings.**

Because of this experience, I spend way more time in the vibration of love. I love being in the silence more than ever. I focus less on the stories, opinions and judgments of right and wrong – more on the lessons and the love. *Energy moving, lessons being learned.* Because of this experience, I have much more compassion and acceptance of others and life as it is.

This book is coming to its close. The fog is slowly lifting and my energy is coming back. I have become wiser and have a few more grey hairs and aches. I continue to integrate all the lessons I learned over the past few years. And I'm sure I'll forget and need to be reminded of these lessons again.

**I often find myself stopping in mid-movement,
asking my Inner Physician; *which way? To the right, left,
backwards, forwards or do nothing and stay put?*
Inner guidance is always there.**

"Life is life," as my mom always said; it will continue to have its ups and downs. Pain is a part of life. In life's pains and imperfections lie the gifts of the soul. Difficult feelings still rise, ugly thoughts pop up sometimes and uncomfortable sensations in the body come up too. I can sit with them longer though and love them in ways I couldn't before. And beyond the pain, I know and trust what is moving me and everything else. *Love is.* In all ways and always, moving everything... *Love is.*

A SOUL'S AWAKENING - PRACTICES

Do one practice a day.
If you enjoy it, circle the practice and
add it to your wellness tool box.

DAY 1 PRACTICE
Higher Self Awareness Visualization

This practice will help you differentiate between your Higher Self and all the false stories and beliefs that your mind makes up about who you are. By shifting your view point from the thinking brain, to the still point within and above (which is a spacious place to observe from) you can become aware of the difference between that which is observing (Higher Self/Awareness) and that which is being observed (personality/soul self/body), which will become more and more apparent.

Find a quiet space where you can relax and go inward. Imagine yourself as if you were an audience member in a movie theatre, and that movie that is playing is the story of your life. See this movie of your life playing on the screen before you and keep noticing that you are not actually the character in the movie, but you are the one watching the character in the movie.

Ponder this for a few moments until you can actually experience the difference between that which is viewing and that which is being viewed. The character on screen is your personality/soul self/body and that which is being viewed. This higher place of observation is your Higher Self/Awareness, your true essence. This Higher Self has been with you in each and every one of your life's experiences. This Higher Self has never judged you or anyone else. This place of Awareness is the essence of unconditional love, acceptance and understanding.

From the Higher Self's perspective, it is easy to see the innocence of the characters on the screen. You can see that the scenes with others are merely events and lessons that are teaching you about love and your capacity to love yourself and others more fully.

In your mind's eye, let the scene rewind to your childhood and all the players, the family you were born into, the neighbors, friends, and so on. As your story unfolds, notice how some of them stay and some of them go. Can you see that you are not in control of the next scene that unfolds in the story line of your soul's movie?

Watch as you, the main character in the movie, grow up. Fast forward to a scene in your elementary school... then high school. Can you see how your soul has its own unique learning style? The show continues as you move on to the next scene in your life at High School. Can you see how your soul has its own unique interests?

Forward to another scene of your first intimate connection. What did you learn in that relationship? Perhaps there were other intimate and close connections that came after that one. Skip to another character that you had a serious relationship with. Perhaps some drama arises in that scene. As you stay connected to the perspective of the Higher Self, notice that there is complete acceptance of this drama. What lessons did you learn?

Continue watching your life story unfold. Watch as you get your first job. Your first home. A partner. Children. Observe with neutrality as the dramas and more opportunities to gain wisdom happen. Perhaps, from those situations, you discover your emotions and how to communicate better. As a result, perhaps you start to love yourself more making yourself a priority, so that your needs are as important as others. Or perhaps you make the needs of others as important as your own. The scenes at times are difficult and challenging, but when you start to observe these scenes from a distance, without attaching to right and wrong, you are able to see the life lessons. Can you see the lessons?

Can you see how you are not in control of the story line and how it is unfolding (and has always unfolded) on its own? Can you have compassion and love your life story, the characters in it, even the difficult situations, as you watch them from the perspective of the observer, your Higher Self? Can you see how each scene or the story was exactly what you needed at that time in your life for your own unique soul's growth? Even the difficult ones? You wouldn't possess the wisdom you have now without all the experiences you've had.

As you watch yourself as the main character, can you see that all the characters were merely playing parts so you could learn and grow? Perhaps you can start to see that you have always done the best you could with the consciousness that you had in that given moment. And perhaps you can see that all the other characters were doing the best they could with the consciousness they had in every given moment. Maybe you can see that all the characters in your life were just playing their parts. Can you see that nothing was ever really personal that has ever happened to you?

Now take a break with a few deep breaths and bring yourself to the scene of life happening right now, in this very moment. From the viewpoint of the observer, from your Higher Self, can you see yourself as the character, lying there reading this book, "Awaken Your Inner Physician?"

The story line continues, however, in this next scene you are experiencing the show. You are experiencing the scenes, and yet you know, your Higher Self is there at all times and is a part of every scene. What is the setting you are in right now? What characters are a big part of the story line you are in now? What are you experiencing and learning right now? Can you stay focused on what you are to learn and do without attaching to all the stories or the players/people? Can you distinguish your Higher Self from the experiences and the story line as it unfolds?

If it feels right, sit for a while and connect to all the love you have around you in this very moment. See if you can accept yourself and life as it is in this moment. Allow yourself to relax and rest as your true essence, your Higher Self, is in an embodied form. Remember this place of love and acceptance is always with you.

DAY 2 PRACTICE
Staying Connected to Your Soul's
Inner Joy Moment to Moment

Give yourself permission to stay in bed or sit and "do nothing" for as long as you like. Your thoughts may be telling you to get up and do things. Don't listen to them, unless they give you total joy. Say to yourself, "I will do only what I love and surrender to my soul's undercurrent of joy."

To connect to your soul's undercurrent of joy, come into your body, and bring your attention to your heart. Ask yourself, what would give me the greatest amount of joy and satisfaction in this moment? Wait and listen.

Wait to see if your body wants to get up or stay still. Maybe you want to meditate, give yourself a massage or gaze out your window at nature's beauty. Keep checking in with your heart. Often times, it is the simple things that give us the most enjoyment: taking a nap, walking in nature, being mindful with our food, taking a warm shower, decorating our bodies with clothes, reading, watching our favorite shows and so on.

If anxiety or fear comes up while doing this practice, see if you can comfort those emotions and remind yourself, "I am safe to do what I love moment to moment." Sometimes we have old conditioning that brings up guilt and fear if we don't do what our thoughts tell us we "should" be doing. Conditioning beliefs that we'll "get in trouble" or that we "need to be productive" come up. This is normal. We've been conditioned to follow other people's joy instead of being true to our own. Due to survival patterns, we developed as a child, we learned to follow the beliefs and desires of our teachers and parents over our own. Therefore, making our own inner voice and following our authentic inner joy is often given a backseat. Your inner voice may be so buried, it may take some serious listening to hear it.

So right now, give yourself permission to really check in to your own heart and body, to that which would give you the greatest joy, moment to moment. Make sure you don't do anything that doesn't bring you pleasure, joy and satisfaction.

1. *Ask yourself, "In this very moment, what will give me the greatest joy?"*

   ----

2. *After you feel satisfied from one experience or activity, continue to ask yourself throughout your day, "What would give me the greatest joy in this very moment?" Is it cooking with creativity, building a project, calling a friend, writing for fun, doing the dishes, stretching and giving my body attention, running errands and getting out and about, or some other hidden interest? "What would I really love doing this moment?"*

As you present the options of what your possibilities are moment to moment, see how your body responds when you bring an activity to mind. Notice how you feel when you walk a certain direction in your home and out in your community. If your body feels peaceful, joyful and expansive, your answer is "yes." If your body contracts and feels tight, the answer is "no." Sometimes the sensing of the "yes" and "no" in the heart and body can be very subtle.

Learning to listen to this inner gauge takes practice. The more you sense and feel it, the louder it will get. Enjoy playing with this moment-to-moment practice as it will bring more inner harmony, joy and satisfaction into your life and the lives of those around you.

DAY 3 PRACTICE
Unconditional Soul-Love Visualization

Imagine your soul being held by a warm, soft, unconditionally loving hand. It holds all of your experiences with understanding, compassion and acceptance. Perhaps there are parts of your journey that you haven't embraced yet. Allow these loving arms to hold even those parts of you that you push away; those experiences that you feel embarrassed or shamed about. Allow those experiences to be held in the most tender, loving way.

Now take several breaths and feel this loving presence surrounding you. Allow this unconditional love to move through each cell of your body and know that it is always available to you.

Every situation that you have ever experienced is part of who you are now. Every experience you've ever had has given you the wisdom, compassion and understanding that you possess today.

Bring this love and acceptance to your body. Every blemish, bump, bulge, scar and wrinkle belong. As difficult as it may be to accept some of these things, remember that everything you've experienced was necessary for the wisdom you've gained. It is all a part of your life's lessons and unique soul's expression.

Take a few more full breaths and see this loving energy running through and around every thought that you have ever had. This love does not judge any of them and holds your essence more important than any of the thoughts that pass through. This love does not attach to thoughts but surrounds each one with love.

This unconditional acceptance cradles every emotion you have ever had and will ever have. It holds the "positive" ones with happiness, joy, love and peace, as well as the "negative" ones with anger, jealousy, disgust and shame. Every thought and every emotion are surrounded by and held with light, love and spaciousness.

1. *Envision your Higher Self unconditionally accepting the gifts that each step in your journey has provided for you.*

Can you name the gifts you have received from various situations, especially the difficult ones?

---

2. *Can you find it within yourself to thank the soul's that have participated in your growth processes, even the ones that provided the most difficult lessons?*

Can you see yourself as an important part of the evolution of this entire universe? Indeed, you are! You are playing your part perfectly and so is everyone else. Bless your journey and those around you.

Now come back to this moment and get ready for your next experience as you center in your Higher Self and loving presence.

HEALTH AND WELL-BEING SUPPORT GROUPS

(Please Note: The word **"FREE"** is placed by resources and groups that offer either free or donation-based activities)

AFFIRMATIONS AS TRUTH REMINDERS

You Can Heal Your Life (1987), **Louise L. Hay.** A book that has healing affirmations for every part of the body, ailments and many diseases. Here is an example of one. "PROBLEM: Heart Attack, PROBABLE CAUSE: Squeezing all the joy out of the heart in favor of money, position, etc. NEW THOUGHT PATTERN: I live in joy, back to the center of my heart. I express love to all."

Emotional Freedom Technique, E.F.T., www.eftuniverse.com. EFT is a powerful self-help method which rapidly reduces the emotional impact of memories and incidents that trigger emotional distress. The process is simple and effective, using tapping techniques and a powerful affirmation. Affirmation: "Even though I am feeling restless, I deeply and completely love and accept myself." Check online for an EFT Practitioner. There are often **FREE** introductory sessions/classes for beginners.

Heart Centered Spiritual Centers and Churches, Interfaith Churches, Synagogues, Ashrams and other community organizations that are all inclusive and about love. Any organization that is accepting of all religions, genders, lifestyles, and focuses on love, kindness and co-creating a world of peace is a part of this list. Through talks, presentations, services, affirmational songs, one can be reminded of their own true essence of love and to have compassion for others, seeing each other as an expression of innocence and love. Often affirmational songs and words are used in services to remind the congregants of their connection to source, inner strength, compassion and building an inclusive, loving and harmonious community. Many gatherings are dona-tion-based or **FREE.**

THOUGHTS, EMOTIONS, PHYSICAL SENSATIONS AND THEIR INTERCONNECTEDNESS

HeartMath Institute, www.heartmath.com. HeartMath has developed reliable, scientifically based tools to help people bridge the connection between their hearts and minds. These tools help individuals honor their emotions, bodies, and access intuitive insights and heart intelligence. Find resources online and a group in your area. Some informal groups that meet up are donation based or **FREE.**

Non-violent Communication **(2003), Marshall Rosenberg, Ph.D.** This book and classes based on this book are about Non-Violent Communication techniques (NVC) and Emotional Intelligence practices for everyday people. The book and classes give you a simple template on how to identify your emotions, your needs and how to make requests to get your needs met and ensure others get their needs met too. The information in this book is powerful, life-changing and if practiced, will affect all your relationships at work, with family and community, in a profound way. There are **FREE** videos online. Group meetings and classes are offered all over the world. Find the classes nearest you.

Choice Theory, Dr. William Glasser, www.wglasser.com. Dr. Wil-liam Glasser (passed in 2013) was a visionary and has written many books: *Choice Theory (1998), Reality Therapy (1965), The Quality School (1998) and Schools Without Failure (1975).* In his books, he advocates for personal power, personal freedom, choice, personal responsibility and inner transformation. His books and work-shops also teach about the interconnectedness of one's emotions, needs and how to get those needs met. "Every behavior is one's best attempt at getting a need met. Is what you are doing getting you what you want?" Check out the William Glasser Institute for workshops and classes nearest you.

Open Focus, www.openfocus.com. This organization has its roots in neuro and bio-feedback techniques. Les Fehmi is one of the primary teachers. Teachers of open focus offer simple suggestions to encourage a relaxed, open focused brain and practices that dissolve mental, emotional and physical pain. Check online for books, workshops and classes. **FREE** Open Focus meditations online.

LOVING, LIFE FORCE ENERGY

Reiki I, II, III. Reiki is an ancient energetic healing modality, using symbols and intention. Reiki heals on many levels, mentally, emotionally and physically. Reiki I offers practices that teach the awareness of energy and how to give and receive loving energy. Reiki II involves information regarding distant energetic healings and deeper emotional and mental healings. Reiki III offers more in-depth skills, especially if you are interested in teaching Reiki. Karuna Reiki came through William Rand and introduces more symbols around compassion and relationship healings. There is information online. However, you can often find local classes near you by checking your community bulletin board, Universities and Colleges. Class costs vary depending on the teacher and level. Reiki practice groups are generally **FREE,** a small fee or a donation is requested.

"Circle of Friends" gatherings, www.bruno-groenig.org. Circle of Friends is an international organization where individuals gather together and relax their minds as they focus on music and "tune in" to a healing stream of energy. Bruno Groenig's (deceased) began these groups in the 1940's and 1950's after World War II in Germany where the origins of these healing gatherings started. There are Circle of Friends meetings in almost every state and country in the world. There are also international gatherings and workshops offered which cost a reasonable fee. However, the monthly Circle of Friends meetings are **FREE,** based on donations only.

Qigong. Qigong has a rich history in China and Taoism. Qigong is a holistic system of coordinated body postures and slow energetic movements. Teachers of Qigong focus on breathing and meditation. Students become aware and cultivate awareness of their life force energy for a strong, healthy body, clear mind and stable emotions. Check out "Qigong" online for classes nearest you. Sometimes individuals offer **FREE** classes in the parks.

Tai Chi. Tai Chi has its roots in Chinese Martial Arts and ancient Chinese medicine. Tai Chi focuses on energy movements that incorporate yin (receiving energy) and yang (giving energy) forms. Tai Chi has many health benefits that can reduce stress, strengthen your body and relax your mind. Classes are offered at community centers and other health clubs.

Acupuncture. Acupuncture is an ancient Chinese form of treatment to help relieve pain, emotionally, mentally and physically. Needles are placed in specific energy meridians depending on the individual's ailments. Acupuncture has become widely accepted in the West and sometimes acupuncture is available through one's Health Care Provider. Community acupuncture clinics are very reasonably priced and affordable. You can also pay a little more for a private session. Check on line for the nearest acupuncture services in your area.

MEDITATION AND MINDFULNESS

Meditation Apps, www.headspace.com, www.insighttimer.com, www.calm.com. These are amazing meditation apps with a library of various types of meditations: breath meditations, visualizations, affirmations and awareness meditations. Just put your head phones on or speaker phone on as you listen to these various meditations. They will help you with deeper relaxation, decreasing anxiety, pain management and are great to listen to before bedtime. They are **FREE**. It you want to upgrade, of course, it costs.

Center for Mindfulness in Medicine and Health Care, John Kabat Zinn. Jon Kabat-Zinn is a meditation and mindfulness teacher and the founder of mindfulness-based stress reduction. He is known for creating the Center for Mindfulness in Medicine, Health Care and the Society at the University of Massachusetts Medical School. Research supports the healing effects of mindfulness-based practices for the mind and body. He has many books and online sources on meditation and mindfulness; just google his name.

Meditation Classes in the Community. Meditation practices have been going on since 3,500 BCE. There are meditation traditions in almost every culture and religion. Meditation and mindfulness practices have been modified over the years to fit our modern-day society. Mindfulness practices have gone mainstream and are now show research-based benefits. Individuals are learning meditation and mindfulness practices though churches, schools, the workplace, healthcare and other centers. Classes and groups teach ways to go inward and connect with one's inner self, calming the mind and body. Forests, rivers, gardens, labyrinths, chapels and other supportive environments are great places to meditate. Go online to find the meditation class nearest you.

Mindful Schools, www.mindfulschools.org. Mindful Schools began in 2007 and is now an international organization supporting schools, children, teachers, common individuals and businesses with various mindfulness practices. They offer research-based mindfulness practices such as mindful bodies, mindful thoughts and mindful emotions, to deepen self-awareness and increase one's well-being. The organization provides class instruction, professional training and other resources to support mindfulness practices in various venues.

Vipassana Meditation. This type of meditation is taught through the Buddhist tradition, but is not religious. The focus is on the body's sensation and having awareness of the body as you mindfully scan it. There are various Vipassana Meditation retreats including a 10-day retreat that is offered in the U.S. and various parts of the world. Food and lodging are included and the first time is **FREE**. It will give you a secure foundation in your daily meditation skills. If you go a second time it is on a donation basis. All other classes and retreats vary in price.

Eckhart Tolle's books and talks, https://bit.ly/EckhartTeachings-FreeResources, *The Power of Now (1997), A New Earth: Awakening to Your Life's Purpose (2005).* Eckhart Tolle is an international teacher and lecturer of awareness, the ego, meditation and of being in the present moment. If you look online, you will see many events and retreats he offers throughout the world. **FREE** meditations, talks and healing resources are also online (you-tube).

INNER INQUIRY QUESTIONS

The Work, www.thework.com, *Loving What Is: The Four Questions (2003), Byron Katie.* Checkout Byron Katie's website and book where she introduces "The Work." She teaches four specific inner inquiry questions that will help turn your negative perspectives around, and give you deeper insights about yourself. Byron Katie calls it "The Work." Her four inner inquiry questions are simple, yet powerful. There are many workshops using these specific turnabout questions to help you become a "lover of reality," a lover of what is. Get the book or go on her website and look for the workshop nearest you.

The Living Inquiries, www.livinginquires.com. This organization, created by Scott Kiloby, has classes and workshops that teach a specific, simple inner inquiry method of unraveling unconscious fears and belief systems. Anything challenging or painful can be explored in this basic mindfulness space. This simple process can bring about a new sense of freedom. There are various teachers, presenters, books, workshops and a recovery center. There are also some **FREE** resources available online.

Contemplating the Nature of Experience, www.rupertspira.com, Rupert Spira. Rupert Spira is a teacher who offers a gentle approach to looking inward. He asks contemplative questions that point you to the true nature of who you are. He focuses on non-duality, the unity of mind and matter and other fascinating topics. He offers classes and workshops. There are some **FREE** videos online and a **FREE** newsletter too.

NATURE AND HEALING VISUALIZATIONS

Reconnecting with Nature **(2007), Michael J. Cohen.** Michael Cohen has written many books and articles about the healing effects of nature. The nature practices at the end of each chapter are healing for the mind and body. "Most of us have been conditioned to ignore more than fifty natural sensitivities that connect us with nature's beauty, health and regenerative ways. This omission underlies our unhealthy stress and disorders." Cohen points us in the direction of sensing energy in nature so that we may receive its healing gifts and connect to our own healthy inner nature.

Nature Guided Visualizations on YouTube. There are plenty of online nature visualizations with waterfalls, rivers, flowers, trees and landscapes that include background music along with positive words to invite you deeper into yourself and bring about an expansive, healing vibration for your body, mind and emotions. Look online under "Nature's Guided Visualizations." There are plenty of **FREE**bies.

Cascadia Quest, www.cascadiaquest.org. Cascadia Quest is located near Eugene, Oregon and offers rites of passage journeys in nature for teens and vision quests for adults. While being out in nature, sharing group activities, and spending time in nature and in the silence, amazing transformations happen. The releasing of old wounds and remembering your true purpose occurs. Then Cascadia Quest organizes a re-entry back into the community as the families come together and welcome those on their vision quest back into society and hear about their transformations. Prices vary. Look for a vision quest adventure near you or come visit Oregon!

Nature Vision Quests, www.questforvision.com. Get away from it all and dive into nature as you discover and experience your authentic self. These nature vision quests offer profound workshops for teens and adults to help them reconnect with nature and with themselves. These Vision Quests help individuals rediscover their passion, purpose and power in their lives. Find your true nature in nature. Check prices and dates on their website.

CONSCIOUS BREATH AS AN ANCHOR

Breath Meditation classes: www.holotropic.com, www.breath-bliss.com, www.healthjourneys.com, www.breathworkonline.com. Check out these websites and the Breath workshops they offer. Breath awareness has long been a healing modality to get individuals out of their busy minds and into their bodies, where they can release the stresses held there. Learn to use the breath to recenter as you release and let go; then relax and receive loving energy and insights. Costs vary.

Breathwork meditations, www.insighttimer.com. Download the Insight Timer app and then search for breath meditations. There are also many other types of meditation such as visualizations, affirmations and so on, for stress, fear, trauma and awareness. They are **FREE** or you can upgrade and pay for a higher subscription.

Transformational Breath Foundation, www.transformational-breathfoundation.com. Breathwork is a simple, and a powerful self-healing practice. Transformational Breath Foundation offers workshops and trainings all over the world. Find the one near you or online.

EMOTIONAL INTELLIGENCE, NEEDS
AND QUALITY COMMUNICATION

Compassionate Communication and Non-violent Communication techniques, https://nvctraining.com, https://heartofnow.org, https://nglcommunity.org, https://thefearlessheart.org, *Non-violent Communication* **(2003), Marshall Rosenberg, Ph.D.** This book and classes teach how to identify your emotions, your needs and how to make requests to get your desires met, along with negotiating strategies so everyone wins. The information in this book is powerful, life-changing and affects all relationships, including your partner, work, family and with your community. Knowing and practicing these tools will shift your life and relationships into satisfying, harmonious connections. Guaranteed! Group meetings, classes and trainings are offered all over the world. There are **FREE** videos online.

Twelve Step Meetings. Bill Wilson and Bob Smith founded the first meeting in 1935 to help alcoholics "stay sober." Now, Twelve Step meetings have multiplied and include various addictions such as ala-non adults, codependent relationships, teens of alcoholics, adult children of alcoholics, sex addicts, narcotics, meth or marijuana, overeating, cluttering, shopaholics and so on. There are too many to name. Look up "Titles of 12 Step Meetings" and find the one that meets your needs. Twelve Step Meetings are held all over the world. These meetings are confidential (anonymous). Twelve Step gathering offer a supportive community and sponsors who will assist you. Sponsors are mentors who can help you grow and are **FREE**. Meetings are **FREE** and donations are accepted.

Human Awareness Institute (HAI), Love, Sexuality and Intimacy Workshops, www.hai.org. HAI offers different level workshops, each level having a different theme. All workshops have counselors and support groups as part of the structure. Workshops are offered in Southern and Northern California, East Coast, Canada, UK, Germany and Australia and still expanding. Look online for workshops near you. After attending a workshop, there are **FREE**

(donation based) support groups. Find the one nearest you after taking a workshop.

Relationship Books and Workshops, www.imagorelationships. org, *Getting the Love You Want (1988). The Couple's Companion (1994). Keeping the Love You Find (1992),* **Harville Hendrix.** These books and workshops give couples and individuals awareness of how we choose intimacy based on our model from our parents. It works like this, the "imago match" has characteristic that match our parents, we unconsciously choose partners that mirror those characteristics. When we identify these conditioned traits, we can shift and our relationship shifts too. Workshops provide greater reflection and understanding so that you can become aware and address these ingrained beliefs and behaviors so you can transform them and be in more satisfying, healthy relationships.

Co-counseling, International, www.cci-usa.org. Co-counseling is a practice firmly established to achieve emotional health, personal clarity and self-fulfillment. After individuals are trained in the co-counseling process, it becomes a peer process where two people have sessions together to help heal past trauma, present pain, and celebrate growth and change. There are **FREE** introductory evenings. And although the classes and workshop cost a modest amount, when you become a co-counselor, you have access to a greater counseling community and your sessions are **FREE.**

Men's Workshops and Men's Groups. Mankind Project, www. mankindproject.org. This organization is a men's world-wide community for transformation and healing. They offer New Warrior Training Workshops for men of all backgrounds, orientations, life-styles, religions, ages and abilities. This non-profit organization supports a global network of facilitated men's groups that focuses on deeper connections to oneself, each other and the community. After taking a workshop, men have an opportunity to be a part of a facilitated men's group ("I" group) in their area which is **FREE** and sometimes donations are given.

Women's Workshops and Groups. Woman Within, www.woman-with.org. Woman Within is a global, organization led by women helping other women to reclaim their wisdom and power. They create a space for women to know themselves, find their authentic voice and to become a force of change for the world. They offer Woman Within Weekends which are a two-and-a half-day experience for women and they offer much, much more. Check out their website.

ZEGG Forum, www.zegg-forum.org. This organization began in 1978. The workshops and gatherings promote awareness, essential communication and trust. Facilitators introduce a transformative process for individuals and groups of various sizes. Groups gather and explore world views of authentic human and ethical values. The activities within the gatherings offer individual expression and opportunities to explore oneself deeper along with shifts from perceiving us as separate individuals to seeing the interconnection of us all. Sometimes there are **FREE** events as well as workshops that are reasonably priced.

Young Men Gatherings. Sacred Sons, www.sacredsons.com. This organization assists in helping young men grow and awaken to their own inner power through gatherings, circles, workshops, retreats, trainings and online courses. Healthy masculinity is taught through ancient wisdom and modern technologies of human development. Prices vary depending on activity and workshops. However, the first two weeks are offered for **FREE** on their app.

INNER RHYTHMS AND AUTHENTIC MOVEMENT

Movement Workshops and Movement as Therapy Trainings. The 5 Rhythms and The Moving Center School, www.5rhythms.com. This organization was founded in 1977 by Gabrielle Roth (deceased). The 5 Rhythms has become a global movement from Montreal, to Koln, Melbourne, Nosara, Denmark, California and New York. Workshops and Teacher training are offered. As well as dances and movement classes are offered by trained 5-Rhythm's teachers in cities around the world. Through movement and connection with others, a therapeutic and a healing environment occurs. It is a way to transform negative belief patterns, chaos and crisis into connection and creativity. Find a workshop or tribe near you.

Ecstatic Dance and Authentic, Healing Movement, www.ecstatic-dance.com. There are many names for Ecstatic Dances, "Sweat Your Prayers, Dance Church, Dance Circle, Inner Rhythms, Coalescence" and so on. This movement has gone global and is in cities all over the United States and the world. These dances are about freedom to express whatever is alive for you and to be accepted in an unconditional loving community. There is no talking on the dance floor and in this way, you will receive insights. The dances are a modern-day meditation with movement, connecting with yourself and others, if you choose. Heart shares at the end of each dance create a beautiful community. All ages and lifestyles welcomed! Check online under "Ecstatic Dance" to find the one nearest you. Often you can do a work-trade of setting up, tearing down, creating altar, etc. for **FREE** admission. However, the cost is very reasonable.

Dances of Universal Peace, www.dancesofuniversalpeace.org. These dances began in the late 1960's led by the late Samuel Lewis, in San Francisco. The dances are simple circle dances using sacred phrases from all spiritual and pagan traditions around the world. No experience or partner needed. The dances use positive affirmations, breath, movement and silence to create a community of connectedness. All ages and lifestyles are welcomed! Donations are asked and is **FREE** for anyone who can't donate.

Yoga classes: Gentle Yoga, Nidra Yoga, Core Strengthening Yoga, Yin Yoga, Restorative Yoga, Chair Yoga and many more. Yoga classes are in most every city now. This practice comes from ancient Spiritual traditions but is now a healthy modern-day practice for many. Yoga uses specific postures, which also include breath practices and simple meditations to promote health and relaxation.

There are many **FREE** resources online. See "Yoga with Adrianne" (you tube). Otherwise, classes vary in costs.

MUSIC, SINGING AND SOUND HEALING

Community Singing. Singing Alive Village, www.singingalive. org. This gathering started in 2007. The annual event on the West Coast brings people together who want to share, sing and bring a higher consciousness to the planet through song and connection. Here, individuals gather to engage in a nourishing, singing community where songs of healing and wholeness are offered. The large community song circle is a gathering for all ages and experience levels. The annual event is very affordable.

Community Singing. Song Village, www.songvillage.net. Song Village is a gathering that happens on the West Coast once a year. Many of the global love community singers are there to share their songs. It is an event for those who want to learn new songs, enjoy community and is also great for those who want to start their own community song circles. It does cost, but is very, very reasonable.

Global Love Artists for Community Song Circles. These artists are all about welcoming the new movement and vision of a healthier planet and a new world where we are all live sustainably with the earth and with each other. Check out *Heather Houston, Sheree Amini, Ma Muse, Beautiful Chorus, Red Molly, Wailin' Jennys, Earth Practice, Karly Loveling and there are a host of other up and coming artists.* Check out some of their songs on YouTube and start your own community song circles.

Threshold Singers, www.thresholdchoir.org. Threshold singers is a worldwide movement to sing to those who are crossing over the threshold of death and their loved ones. The singers practice in a larger group and then go out in threes or fours and sing gentle and compassionate songs for individuals nearing end of life. Some skill is needed. To request singers for your loved ones or to join a group, look online at thresholdchoir.org nearest you. The services of song to others are **FREE**. To join the group, a small cost annually for the use of the international website and their songs is required. Singers/members practice bi-monthly or sometimes they have weekly practices. The practices are usually **FREE** or is donation based, depending on the cost of the facility used to practice in.

Sound Healing Events. These events focus on sound healing using singing bowls, gongs, digeridoos, drumming, hand pans, and other healing instruments. By allowing your mind to relax and open, a calmer frequency occurs which affects the alpha, beta and delta brainwaves in a positive way. Check online for events around you.

Many Healing Music Artists and Concerts. Music that is positive, relaxing, uplifting and meaningful is popping up all over through various artists. Download your own favorite music and make your own healing music playlists to listen to. Here are a few old and new names that sing uplifting, healing music: Michael Franti, Yanni, Wah, Ashana, Imaging Heat, Ayla Nereo, Snatam Kaur, Yaima, East Forest, Jaiuttal, Will Tuttle, Eric Bibb, Suzanne Teng, Alexi Murdoch, Alice Walker, Anilah, Jennifer Berezan, Karen Drucker, India Arie, Atman, Benjy Wertheimer, Bob Marley, Crystal Voices, Dean Evenson, Dessert Dwellers, Deva Premal & Milton, Enya, Estaban, Evenson & Xiangling & Heather Houston… and of course, there are a host of other up and coming artists. Check them out on line on you-tube, **FREE**.

Drumming Circles. Drumming Circles can range in size from a handful of drummers to hundreds of drummers. Various hand drums and percussion drumming instruments are used. Usually, there is no main leader, therefore no head or tail. Individuals listen to each other and play spontaneously from a place of connection which brings them in the present moment. In general, drumming circles include all ages. Look online for a drumming circle in your area or start one yourself. The cost is usually **FREE**, donation or a small fee is asked to cover facility expenses, but often drumming events are held in the park.

PRESENT TOUCH AND MASSAGE

Therapeutic Touch and Healing Touch, therapeutictouch.org and www.healingtouchprogram.com Therapeutic touch uses a gentle approach where hands are placed softly on an individual's shoulders, hands and feet as loving intention and energy flows through for healing. Healing Touch is similar, except it is a "non-contact" activity, where hands are held ABOVE the individual shoulders, hands and feet as loving intention and healing energy flows. They both rely on evidence-based universal energy therapy which promotes healing in all aspects of the individual, body, mind and spirit. The sessions reduce anxiety and pain and promote balance and well-being. Simple classes are offered in this healing form of presence. Look on line for a class, practitioner or group where individuals practice together. Therapeutic Touch and Healing Touch certifications and programs are offered; check out their websites.

Massages and Bodywork. Receiving bodywork from a specialist who is trained in various modalities, such as Reiki, pressure points, deep tissue and Swedish massage can open areas in your body that are tight and also affect your emotional and mental well-being. You can hire a massage therapist to teach you and your partner/friends some self-massage techniques, as well. Massages range in price depending on the massage therapist's experience. Talk to your friends to see who they might recommend. Or look up massage and bodywork online in your area.

The FeldenKrais Method, www.feldenkrais.com. The process was developed by Dr. Moshe Feldenkrais (passed away in 1984). This method uses gentle, mindful movement by a trained, somatic practitioner to bring new insights as they assist in opening the body-mind connection. The method helps with postural control and balance, pain relief, movement difficulties and provides healthy aging. It is a powerful and revolutionary approach and brings in awareness into all areas of your life.

Breema, www.breema.com. Breema has been described as a cross between partner yoga and Thai massage. The techniques may be used with either in a practitioner-client basis or individually by yourself. Its intention is to bring the body and mind together. There is no force or high exertion. Find a Breema practitioner in your area.

Contact Improvisation, www.contactimprov.com. Contact Improv is an activity that came from Aikido and modern dance. It is a form of improvised movement, play, safe touch that promote connection with friends, families and partners. There are many contact jams, events and workshops around the world. Look online for the classes nearest you.

BIBLIOGRAPHY AND
OTHER SOURCES READ

Abraham-Hicks, Esther and Jerry, A quote on a Well-Being card. Well-Being Cards, TX 2012.

Center for Self-Transformation Breathwork Manual and Training, Sacramento, CA 2001.

Charde', LaShelle, "Wise Heart," Handout at NVC group in Eugene, OR. Web. June 2006 http;//www.wiseheartpdx.org

Co., Stephen, Robin MD & Eric, 2002. *Your Hands Can Heal You.* New York: Free Press.

Cohen, Michael J., 2007. *Reconnecting With Nature (Third Edition).* Ecopress: Lakeville, MN.

Cowan, Megan, "Mindful Schools," Learning Conference. Santa Cruz, CA. Oct. 2013, and Web. Aug 2014 http://www. innovativelearningconference.org

Beattie, Melody, 1987. *Codependent No More: How to Stop Controlling Others & Start Caring For Yourself,* San Francisco: Harper & Row Publishers, p. 229.

Begley, Sharon 2007. *Train Your Mind. Change Your Brain.* New York: Ballentine Books.

Benson, Herbert, 2000. *The Relaxation Response.* New York: Avon Books.

Brumet, Robert J. M.S., "Insight Meditation Keeps Us in the Now," Unity Contact Magazine, Aug./Sept. 2008.

Bradshaw, John, 1990. *HomeComing: Reclaiming and Championing Your Inner Child,* New York: Bantam Books, N.Y.

Bryson, Kelly MFT, 2004. *Don't Be Nice Be Real.* Santa Rosa, CA: Elite Books.

Campbell, Colin, T. Ph D. and Campbell, Thomas, 2006. *The China Study.* Dallas TX: Benbella Books.

Clay, James H. & Pounds, David M. *Basic Clinical Massage Therapy: Integrating Anatomy and Treatment.* New York; Lippincott Williams & Wilkins Co, 2003

Crawford, John, "Why Natural Medicine?" Fair Oaks, CA: Crawford Natural Health Center Bulletin, 2003

Dejean, Valerie and Freer, Alex, "The Tomatis Method of Auditory Stimulation: An Overview," Sacramento, CA: The Listening Clinic Brochure, Feb. 2006.

Douglas, Inge and Ellis, Suzanne, 1992. *The Art of Reflexology.* Rockport, MA: Element Books Inc.

"Eating Intuitively," Web. 13 Aug. 2004, http//www. livingspiritfoundation.org

Emoto, Masaru, 2001. *The Hidden Messages in Water.* New York: Atria Books

Fiddmont, Valerie Joi, "Singing Circle, Practicing the Principles," Inner Light Ministries, Aptos, CA 95003, (2010).

Free, Valerie, "Far-Infrared:Technologies that Harness the Sun," Complimentary Healing, pp. 5-12, 2007

Emotional Freedom Technique Workshop, Unity of the Valley, Eugene, Oregon, 2009.

Gerber, Richard, M.D., 2001. *Vibrational Medicine* (Third Edition). Rochester, VT: Bear & Co. p.67.

Glasser, William, M.D., 2001. *Choice Theory in the Classroom.* New York: Quill-Harper Collins Publishers.

Gonzales, Robert, "NVC as a Spiritual Practice," Handout. http// www.living-compassion.org, 2010.

Hay, Louise L., 1987. *You Can Heal Your Life*. Carlsbad, CA: Hay House Inc.

Halpern, Steven, "Healing Music is Sound Medicine," TM, Inner Peace Music Catalog, 2012.

Hawkins, David R. M.D., Ph.D., 2002. *Power VS. Force*. Carlsbad, CA: Hay House, Inc.

Hicks, Abraham-Esther, 1997. *The Science of Deliberate Creation*. Abraham-Hicks Publications, San Antonio, TX 78269.

Hillard, Ellyn. "Natural health Care vs. Traditional Medicine?" Sac., CA: Community Forum at Local Bookstore, 2004.

Johnson, Deborah L., "Helpful Hints on Affirmations,. Aptos, CA: Inner Light Ministries Handout, 2002.

Jones, Rebecca, "The Body Knows," Body Sense, Autumn/Winter, 2009.

Kabat-Zinn, Jon. "The Art of Teaching Mindfulness," YouTube, Aug. 16, 2014.

Kaiser Permanente Pamphlet, Sacramento, CA: 2008

Katie, Byron, 2001. *Loving What Is*. New York: Three Rivers Press.

Kaur, Snatam, "People of Love," Celebrate Peace CD on Amazon

Klein, Nancy M.A., 2001. *Healing Images for Children*, Watertown, WI: Inner Coaching Publishing.

Levitin, Daniel, 2006. *This Is Your Brain On Music*. New York: A Plume Book.

Lohaus, A., Kein-Hessling. J., Vogele, C., & Kuhn-Henninghausen, C., "Psychophysiological Effect of Relaxation Training in Children," British Journal of Health Psychology, 6, 197-206, 2001.

Mally, James, CMT, MA. Healing Arts Massage School, Roseville, Notes from lecture, 1998.

Means, Linda G. Ph.D., C.M.T., "Dimensions of Holistic Massage," Massage and Bodywork Magazine, Nov/Dec 2009.

Miller, Angelyn, 1988. *The Enabler: When Helping Harms The Ones You Love*. Claremont, CA: Hunter House Inc.

"Mindfulness Going Mainstream," PBS Television, 10:00pm, Eugene, OR, June 6, 2018.

Mindful Schools, Mindful Schools presentation at Gateway Schools, Santa Cruz, CA 2001

Miranda, A., "Efficacy of Cognitive Behavioral Therapy in the Treatment of Children with ADHD," Psychology in the Schools, 37, 169-183, 2006.

Miller, Emmit Ph. D., "Changing Your Behaviors," Auburn, CA: Deep Healing Source Newsletter, 2003.

Osborn, Karrie, "Massage Multiplied," Body Sense Magazine, Autumn/Winter, 2009.

Oz, Mehmet M.D. and Roizen, Mike M.D., "Yoga Boosts Your Brain Power," Eugene, OR: Register Guard, February 8, 2020, B5.

Redman, Jeffrey "Page", "A History of Edgu," instructional DVD. Breightenbush, OR, 2006.

Reichenber-Ullman J. & Ullman R., 1996. *Ritalin Free Kids: Safe and effective medicine for ADD and other behavioral and learning problems*. Rocklin, CA: Prima Publishing.

Rengel, Peter, MA. Quote by HAI 1. Presenter and Counselor for Human Awareness Institute, Harbin Hots Springs, CA., 2001.

Rosenfeld, Arthur, "Longevity Tai Chi," CPTV Media Video, www. http://dptvmedia.org, 2010.

Rose, Mary Kathleen & Foster, Mary Ann, "Grounding a Body-Mind Practice," Massage & Bodywork Magazine, Nov./ Dec. 2009, p. 27.

Rodegast, Pat & Stanton, Judith, 1987. *Emmanuel's Book: A Manual for Living Comfortably.* New York: Bantam Books.

Rodegast, Pat & Stanton, Judith. 1989. *Emmanuel's Book II: The Choice for Love.* New York: Bantam Books.

Rosenberg, Marshall Ph.D., 2003. *Nonviolent Communication.* (Second Edition) Encinitas, CA: Puddle Dancer Press.

Roth, Gabrielle, 1998. *Maps to Ecstasy.* Novato, CA: New World Library, Nataraj Publishing.

Schneider, Meir PhD, L.MT., 2004. *Movement for Self-Healing.* Novato, CA: New World Library.

Schucman, Helen, 1972. *Course in Miracles,* Text; Workbook for Student, Manuscript for Teachers, Foundation For Inner Peace, P.O. Box 1104, Glen Ellen, CA 95442.

Simonton, O. Carl, Stephanie Matthews-Simonton, and James L. Creighton, 1978. *Getting Well Again.* New York: Bantam Books.

Simon, David, "Return to Wholeness: Embracing Body, Mind, and Spirit in the Face of Cancer," New York: John Wiley & Sons, 1999.

Smith, Laurie Chance, "Massage and Body Image," Massage & Bodywork, March/April 2009, p. 33.

Sovik, Rolf, "Become Your Own Inner Witness," Yoga International. Web. July 4, 2014 Htp//www.facebook.com.

Swindoll, Charles, "Attitude: It's Mostly Mind Over Matter," Sac., CA: Foster Youth Services Newsletter, 1996.

Taylor, Eldon Ph.D., 1999. *New Cognitive Therapy Successful with ADHD.* Medical Lake, WA.

Tomatis, 2006, "The Tomatis Method," The Listening Center Pamphlet. Sacramento, CA

Unity Churches, "Affirmations and Reminders," Unity of Sacramento Bulletin, Sacramento, CA, 1992-2008.

Van, Gerilyn & Ransom, Bobby, "Practicing Presence – Contact Improv," DVD-2016, Santa Cruz, CA 95061.

Van, Gerilyn, "Abundant Love Breath-Meditation," CD-2014, Santa Cruz, CA 95061.

Weintraub, N.D., 1997. *Natural Treatments for ADD and Hyperactivity.* Pleasant Grove, UT: Woodland Publishing.

Williams, Anne, "Is Swedish Massage Dead?" Massage & Bodywork magazine, p. 41, Nov./ Dec. 2009.

Williamson, Marianne, 1994. *Illuminata.* Random House, New York, N.Y.

Yavelow, Andrew, "How to Feel Better In Your Body," Harbin Hot Springs Workshop Handout, Middletown, CA 2013.

Zimmerman, Katherine CHT. "Learn to Love Yourself," Fair Oaks, CA. 2003.

Zukav, Gary, 1990. *The Seat of the Soul.* Simon and Schuster, New York, N.Y.

Beginning Chapter Quotes

I. Thomas S. Monson

II. Ann Hillman

III. Valerie Joi Fiddmont

IV. Angeles Arrien

V. Stephen Lewis

VI. Eckhart Tolle

VII. Albert Einstein

VIII. Abraham, Esther Hicks

IX. Thich Nhat Hahn

X. Peter Rangel

XI. Gabrielle Roth

XII. Nancy Klein

XIII. Cathy Morancy

XIV. Marianne Williamson

ACKNOWLEDGEMENTS

IT'S BEEN AN AMAZING JOURNEY WRITING *AWAKEN YOUR INNER PHYSICIAN... the "Missing Links" in Health Care.* Such a surrendering process to the greater good with many helpers and guides along the way. I am so grateful to all of you, for your suggestions and support throughout these ten years of writing, editing and publishing.

A big thank you to my friend, Annelise Schinzinger, who was one of my first writing partners and a huge support. We spent two and a half years together, fine tuning the structure of the book and editing in the park, at her home, my home and over the phone.

Heartfelt thanks to my mom, Twyla Elkins (deceased), who was willing to edit the book and has always supported my creative adventures. And to my step-dad, Fred Elkins, who handed me a book one day, saying "this is for you." That book shifted the direction and format of this book in a huge way. .

A warmhearted thank you to all the readers for their comments and edits, big and small. Your feedback was invaluable and has improved the book in subtle and dynamic ways: Lisa Tyree Hardin, Karen Berchtold, Jasmine Grace, Maggie Medlin, Jennifer C. Smith, Laura Zuke, Florence Hecker, Daryl Kay Driskill, Cindy Zarzvcki, Ruselle Revenaugh and Dennis Wheeler.

Many thanks to Sally J. Crum, for her heartfelt wisdom. And for her partner, Perry Bream, who passed away during this editing process, for his poetic expression and language expertise. Thank you for all your suggestions and for the times we all spent in your garden perfecting various parts of the book.

A special thanks to Kasondra Lynn Vanpykeren-Gerth, my daughter. Thank you for all your comments and smart editing. I love our connection and the way you have supported me through this writing process and the creation of my books.

Gratitude to Lorre Thompson Lucas for her unwavering support, speedy reading, positive remarks about the book. You will always be in my heart, soul sister.

I thank Donna Louise Stevens, who is one of my profound soul connections, for being the final copy editor and for her outstanding eye for details, truth and clarity.

Additional thanks to Luminare Press, Patricia and Kim for shepherding me through book publication, to Melissa for creating a lovely cover design and exceptional skills with formatting and book design.

ABOUT THE AUTHOR

GERILYN VAN, MA, CMT, RMT, CYT IS THE AUTHOR OF *Awaken Your Inner Physician ... the "Missing Links" in Health Care.* She has been a workshop facilitator in the field of Holistic Health for over 30 years. With a Master's in Education and two teaching credentials, Gerilyn holds the titles of Certified Massage Therapist, Breathwork coach, Reiki Master teacher, Certified Yoga teacher, and Meditation and Mindfulness instructor. Her career began as a public-school teacher and evolved into her own life-coaching and well-being private practice. Gerilyn has offered a variety of community health and wellness workshops including: Reiki and Energy Awareness, Oneness with Nature, "Tuning in" with Meditation, One Heart Contact Improv, Understanding Love-Sex-Intimacy, Partner-Friendship Yoga, and Quality Communication for Couples.

Well into her career, Gerilyn faced the greatest health challenge of her life. She experienced severe chronic pain for two and half years. Her journey through pain was the impetus for the book, *Awaken Your Inner Physician.* The book tells her authentic story and includes practices at the end of each chapter, that she gathered throughout her life to deal with physical pain, mental health and emotional well-being.

Addressing the "Missing Links" in our School's Health Education programs has become Gerilyn's greatest purpose. She is a visionary who sees the possibilities of instilling in our children holistic life-skills to deal with mental, emotional and physical pain in healthy, integrated ways. By giving children much needed skills for self-awareness, Gerilyn believes societal problems and issues such as the opioid crisis, mental illness and suicide among teens, and the lack of emotional intelligence (which has led to so much unnecessary violence such as school shootings), could be addressed, reversed and resolved. She hopes to be a part of a dynamic team that creates a K-12, Integrated Health curriculum, designed to teach our children the critical health and wellness skills that are missing in public schools and in our Health Care System.

Currently, Gerilyn enjoys offering private sessions for couples and individuals, as a Relationship-Life Coach. With an open heart and her converted van, Gerilyn travels for a portion of the year, bringing her books and wisdom to other communities. She is available for book signings, public speaking engagements, and individual and couples counseling sessions.

Visit www.AwakenYourInnerPhysician.com for information, bookings and consultations.

Made in the USA
Columbia, SC
28 June 2022

62387190R00139